For Kate
from Linda

HORSES SELDOM B⬤RP!

Other books by Don Blazer

Training The Western Show Horse
Natural Western Riding
Horses Don't Care About Women's Lib

HORSES SELDOM BRP!

HOW TO KEEP THEM HAPPY AND WELL

DON BLAZER

SAN DIEGO
A. S. BARNES & COMPANY, INC
IN LONDON:
THE TANTIVY PRESS

First Edition
Manufactured in the United States of America

For information write to:

A. S. Barnes & Company, Inc.
P.O. Box 3051
La Jolla, California 92038

Library of Congress Cataloging in Publication Data

Blazer, Don, 1939–
    Horses seldom burp!

    1. Horses.   2. Horses—Diseases.   I. Title.
SF285.3.B55   636.1'089   81-20589
ISBN 0-498-02575-6   AACR2

1   2   3   4   5   6   7   8   9   85   84   83   82

To my special lady, Judi

Contents

Preface

This book is not a complete anything.

It's just a book that will help you get through 20 or more years of owning a horse. By that time — maybe sooner — you'll know nothing is ever complete with horses, except love.

You'll find the book is a handy reference.

You should find this book is a lot like owning a horse: educational and enjoyable; never stuffy, too serious, or pompous.

HORSES SELDOM BURP!

1

So You've Got One

So you've got a large, solid-hoofed quadruped domesticated since prehistoric times and employed as a beast of draft and burden *or* for carrying a rider.

You've got an *Equus caballus*.

You've got one of those things for which there are no fewer than 78 registries in the United States.

You've got companionship, hardship, joy, frustration, relaxation, hard work, and investment and bills, and a lot of arguments as to what you've got.

If you go by the breed association standards of conformation, it's pretty hard to tell what you've got. For the most part, the conformation standards are worded identically.

If you go by the "purity of blood" to determine breed, then it's impossible to determine what you've got. There are no fewer than 16 part-blood or "breed by performance" associations.

There's an American Indian Horse Registry. That's logical. But I don't know what an American Indian Horse is, since the American Indians didn't have horses until the Spanish brought theirs in the 1500s. Maybe you can't have an American Indian Horse unless you're an American Indian?

There are also American Mustangs. It's easier to spot a Ford Mustang than an American Mustang.

There's an American Bay Horse Registry and there's an American Bay Horse Association. Of course, there are Bay horses in every breed, except those distinguished exclusively by color, such as American Creme or American White, or Palomino, or Buckskin, or Paint, or Pinto, all of which have their own associations.

Then there are those associations that deal exclusively with what the horse does, such as Endurance Horse, or Hunter and Jumper, or Miniature Horse, or Walking Pony, or Trottingbred.

With few exceptions, all the associations basically say your horse should have a head of average size — proportionate to the horse in total. He should have large eyes with large pupils. The eyes should be set well out to the side of the head.

The nostrils should be fairly large so that the horse breathes freely. The ears should be of average size with a nice little curve in at the ends and with nice points. (Unless, of course, you are speaking of Burros, Spotted Asses, Donkeys, Mules, Jacks, or Jennets, all of which have their own registries, and are *Equus asinas*.)

The horse should have a broad forehead, a well-defined jawline, long neck, not be heavy in the crest, and have a fine throatlatch.

The shoulders should slope at about 45 degrees.

A short back is desirable, as is a long underline.

The hindquarters should be strong and the croup should be long and fairly level, giving good muscle over the hips. The muscle at the rear of the hindquarters should extend well down into the gaskin area. The rear legs, when "squared," should be in a straight line from the buttock to the hock of the pastern, when viewed from the side.

The hocks should be wide when viewed from the side. They should not be too far apart, or too close. The rear legs should be straight when viewed from behind.

Each pastern should be at just about a 45-degree angle to match the shoulder, as should each hoof.

Hoofs should be basically U-shaped, with fair depth at the rear quarter and the same degree of slope on the inside as on the outside.

The knees should be fairly large and flat, neither being back nor over when viewed from the side. The fetlock joints should appear strong, but not overly large.

A lot of horses approximate those standards, but even if your horse does you still can't be sure what you've got. (Take your horse into the show ring several times and you'll wonder what the judge sees you don't.)

After you can look at your horse without prejudice, and see his good qualities and his bad, and after you no longer care what the registries say you've got, then you've got a whole lot of something very special.

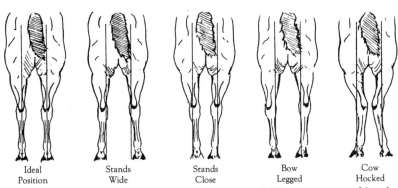

| Ideal Position | Stands Wide | Stands Close | Bow Legged | Cow Hocked |

Vertical line from point of buttock should fall in center of hock, cannon, pastern, and foot.

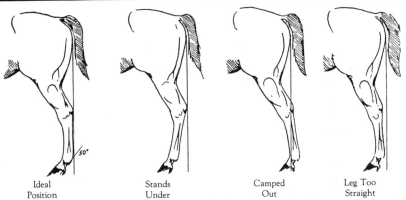

| Ideal Position | Stands Under | Camped Out | Leg Too Straight |

Vertical line from point of buttock should touch the rear edge of cannon from hock to fetlock and meet the ground behind the heel.

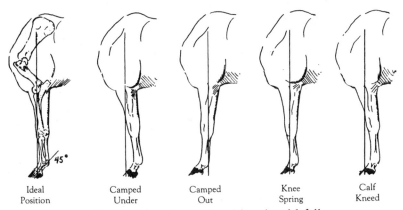

| Ideal Position | Camped Under | Camped Out | Knee Spring | Calf Kneed |

Vertical line from shoulder should fall through elbow and center of foot.

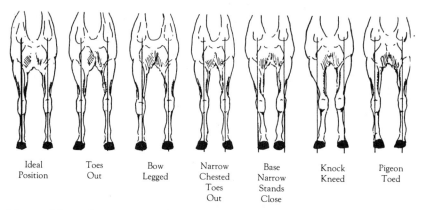

| Ideal Position | Toes Out | Bow Legged | Narrow Chested Toes Out | Base Narrow Stands Close | Knock Kneed | Pigeon Toed |

Vertical line from point of shoulder should fall in center of knee, cannon, pastern, and foot.

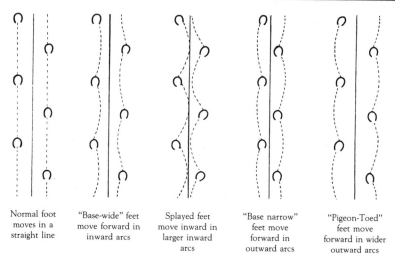

| Normal foot moves in a straight line | "Base-wide" feet move forward in inward arcs | Splayed feet move inward in larger inward arcs | "Base narrow" feet move forward in outward arcs | "Pigeon-Toed" feet move forward in wider outward arcs |

Path of the feet as seen from above

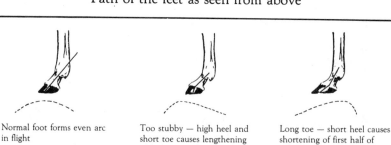

Normal foot forms even arc in flight

Too stubby — high heel and short toe causes lengthening of first half of stride, long heel touches ground earlier which shortens last half of stride.

Long toe — short heel causes shortening of first half of stride and lengthening of last half of stride.

BREED REGISTRIES

AMERICAN INDIAN HORSE REGISTRY
Route 1, Box 64
Lockhart, TX 78644
(512) 398-2090

ANDALUSIAN/LUSITANO
Andalusian Horse Registry of the Americas
Glenn O. Smith
Box 1290
Silver City, NM 88061
(505) 538-9249

APPALOOSA HORSE CLUB, INC.
P.O. Box 8403
Moscow, ID 83843
(208) 882-5578

ARABIAN HORSE REGISTRY OF AMERICA, INC.
3435 South Yosemite Street
Denver, CO 80231
(303) 750-5626

HALF-ARABIAN/ ANGLO-ARABIAN
International Arabian Horse Assoc.
P.O. Box 4502
Burbank, CA 91503
(213) 846-5042

BASHKIR CURLY
American Bashkir Curly Registry
Box 453
Ely, NV 89301
(702) 289-4228

BAY
American Bay Horse Registry
P.O. Box 67
Ashland, OR 97520

American Bay Horse Assoc.
P.O. Box 884F
Wheeling, IL 60090
(312) 537-4830

BELGIAN
Belgian Draft Horse Corp. of America
P.O. Box 334
Wabash, IN 46992

BUCKSKIN
American Buckskin Registry Assoc., Inc.
P.O. Box 1125
Anderson, CA 96007
(916) 365-3160

International Buckskin Horse Assoc., Inc.
P.O. Box 357
St. John, IN 46373
(219) 365-8326

CHICKASAW
Chickasaw Horse Assoc., Inc.
Box 607
Love Valley, NC 28667
(704) 592-7451

CLEVELAND BAY
Cleveland Bay Society of America
P.O. Box 182
Hopewell, NJ 08525
(609) 921-6516

CLYDESDALE
Clydesdale Breeders of the U.S.
Route 1, Box 131
Pecatonia, IL 61063
(815) 247-8780

CONNEMARA PONY
American Connemara Pony Society
HoshieKon Farm
R.D. 1
Goshen, CT 06756
(203) 491-3521

CREME & WHITE
American Creme Horse
American White Horse
P.O. Box 79
Crabtree, OR 87335
(503) 928-9907 (winter)
(402) 832-5560 (summer)

CROSSBRED PONY
American Crossbred Pony Registry
Box M
Andover, NJ 07821
(201) 786-5866

ENDURANCE HORSE
Endurance Horse Registry of America
P.O. Box 63
Agoura, CA 91301
(213) 991-2818

FOX TROTTER
American Fox Trotting Horse Breed Assoc.
Box 666
Marshfield, MO 65706
(417) 468-4012

Missouri Fox Trotting Horse Breed Assoc.
P.O. Box 637
Ava, MO 65608
(417) 683-2468

GALICENO
Galiceno Horse Breeders Assoc.
111 East Elm Street
Tyler, TX 75702
(214) 593-7341

GOTLAND HORSE
American Gotland Horse Assoc.
RR. 2, Box 181
Elkland, MO 65644
(417) 345-7004

HACKNEY HORSE & PONY
American Hackney Horse Society
P.O. Box 174
Pittsfield, IL 62363
(217) 285-2472

HAFLINGER
Haflinger Assoc. of America
2624 Bexley Park Road
Bexley, OH 43209
(614) 221-4671

HANOVERIAN
The American Hanoverian Society
809 West 106th Street
Carmel, IN 46032
(317) 244-7251

HOLSTEIN HORSE
American Holstein Horse Assoc., Inc.
12 Southlawn Ave.
Dobbs Ferry, NY 10522
(914) 693-5722

HORSE OF THE AMERICAS
Horse of The Americas Registry
248 N. Main Street
Porterville, CA 93257
(209) 781-1225

HUNTER & JUMPER
American Hunter & Jumper Assoc.
P.O. Box 1174
Fort Wayne, IN 46801
(219) 744-0672

LIPIZZANER
Royal International Lipizzaner
Club of America, Inc.
Route 7
Columbia, TN 38401
(615) 388-4045

MINIATURE HORSE
International Miniature Horse Registry
P.O. Box 907
Palos Verdes Estates, CA 90274
(213) 375-1898

MORAB
Morab Horse Registry of America
P.O. Box 143
Clovis, CA 93613
(209) 439-5437

MORGAN
American Morgan Horse Assoc., Inc.
P.O. Box 1
Westmoreland, NY 13490
(315) 736-8306

MOROCCO SPOTTED
Morrocco Spotted Horse Assoc. of America
Route 1
Ridot, IL 61067
(815) 449-2659

MUSTANG
American Mustang Assoc.
P.O. Box 338
Yucaipa, CA 92399

NORWEGIAN FJORD
Norwegian Fjord Horse Assoc. of
North America
29645 N. Callahan Rd.
Round Lake, IL 60073
(312) 526-3100

PAINT
American Paint Horse Assoc.
P.O. Box 18519
Fort Worth, TX 76118
(817) 439-3400

PALOMINO
Palomino Horse Assoc., Inc.
P.O. Box 324
Jefferson City, MO 65102
(314) 635-5511

Palomino Horse Breeders of America
P.O. Box 249
Mineral Wells, TX 76067
(817) 325-2848

PART-BLOOD
American Part-Blooded Horse Registry
4120 S.E. River Drive
Portland, OR 97222
(503) 654-6204

PASO FINO
Paso Fino Owners & Breeders Assoc.
P.O. Box 1579
Tryon, NC 28782
(704) 894-3200

PERCHERON
Percheron Assoc. of America
Route 1
Belmont, OH 43718
(614) 782-1624

PERUVIAN PASO
American Assoc. of Owners & Breeders
of Peruvian Paso Horses
P.O. Box 2035
California City, CA 93505
(415) 531-5082

American Peruvian Paso Horse Registry
Route 3, Box 3318
Boerne, TX 78006
(512) 755-4437

Peruvian Paso Horse Registry of
North America
P.O. Box 816
Guerneville, CA 95446
(707) 869-2818

HALF-PERUVIAN PASO
Peruvian Paso Half-Blood Assoc.
43058 North 42nd Street, West
Lancaster, CA 93534
(805) 934-4004

PINTO
Pinto Horse Assoc. of America, Inc.
7525 Mission Gorge Road, Suite C
San Diego, CA 92120
(714) 286-1570

PONY OF THE AMERICAS
Pony of the Americas Club, Inc.
P.O. Box 1447
Mason City, IN 50401
(515) 424-1586

QUARTER HORSE
American Quarter Horse
2736 West Tenth Street
Amarillo, TX 79168
(806) 376-4811

Model Quarter Horse Assoc.
P.O. Box 396
Lincoln, CA 95648

National Quarter Horse Registry
Box 235
Raywood, TX 77582
(713) 587-4341

Standard Quarter Horse Assoc.
4390 Fenton Street, Room 206
Denver, CO 80212
(303) 422-5188

HALF-QUARTER HORSE
Half-Quarter Horse Registry
43949 North 60th West
Lancaster, CA 93534
(805) 943-4689

QUARTER PONY
American Quarter Pony Assoc.
c/o Linda Grim, Secretary
New Sharon, IN 50207
(515) 528-2905

National Quarter Pony Assoc., Inc.
Route 1, Box 585
Marengo, OH 43334
(419) 864-7156

RACKING HORSE
Racking Horse Breeders Assoc. of America
Joe D. Bright
Helena, AL 35080
(205) 988-3733

RANGERBRED
Colorado Ranger Horse Assoc., Inc.
7023 Eden Mill Road
Woodbine, MD 21797

SADDLEBRED
American Saddle Horse Breeders Assoc.
929 South Fourth Street
Louisville, KY 40203
(502) 585-2425

HALF-SADDLEBRED
The Half-Saddlebred Registry of America
660 Poplar Street
Coshocton, OH 43812
(614) 622-1090

SHETLAND PONY
American Shetland Pony Club
P.O. Box 435
Fowler, IN 47944
(317) 884-1242

SHIRE
American Shire Horse Assoc.
14410 High Bridge Road
Monroe, WA 98272
(206) 794-4037

SPANISH-BARB
Spanish Barb Breeders Assoc.
P.O. Box 7479
Colorado Springs, CO 80907
(605) 745-4438

STANDARDBRED
U.S. Trotting Assoc.
750 Michigan Avenue
Columbus, OH 43215
(614) 224-2291

SUFFOLK
American Suffolk Horse Assoc.
15B Roden
Wichita Falls, TX 76311
(817) 855-6998

TARPAN
American Tarpan Studbook Assoc.
Route 6, Box 429
Griffin, GA 30223
(404) 228-7199

THORCHERON
The Thorcheron Hunter Assoc.
3749 South 4th Street
Kalamazoo, MI 49009
(616) 375-1452

THOROUGHBRED
The Jockey Club
380 Madison Avenue
New York, NY 10017
(212) 599-1919

THOROUGHBRED HALF-BRED
American Remount Assoc., Inc.
P.O. Box 1066
Perris, CA 92370
(714) 657-5210

TRAKEHNER
American Trakehner Assoc., Inc.
P.O. Box 132
Brentwood, NY 73070
(405) 360-1612

North American Trakehner Assoc.
Box 100
Bath, OH 44210
(216) 836-9545

TROTTINGBRED
International Trotting and Pacing Assoc.
575 Broadway
Hanover, PA 17331
(717) 637-5777

WALKING HORSE
International Walking Horse Registry
203 Plaza South
630 South Church Street
Murfreesboro, TN 37130
(615) 890-9121

Tennessee Walking Horse Breeders' and
Exhibitors' Assoc.
P.O. Box 286
Lewisburg, TN 37091
(615) 359-1574

WALKING PONY
American Walking Pony Assoc.
Route 5, Box 88
Upper River Road
Macon, GA 31211
(912) 743-2321

WELSH PONY
Welsh Pony Society of America
P.O. Box 2977
Winchester, VA 22601
(703) 667-6195

WILD HORSES/BURROS
Wild Horses of America Registry, Inc.
11790 Deodar Way
Reno, NV 89506
(702) 972-1989

AMERICAN COUNCIL OF SPOTTED ASSES
P.O. Box 21
Fishtail, MT 59028

AMERICAN DONKEY & MULE SOCIETY, INC.
Route 5, Box 65
Denton, TX 76201
(817) 382-6854

STANDARD JACK & JENNET REGISTRY OF AMERICA
300 Todds Road
Lexington, KY 40511
(606) 266-1504

What Gives Him the "Power"?

When you're young you think muscles are necessary to keep sand from being kicked in your face. When you're older, you are sure muscles are for harboring aches and pains.

Actually the muscles of all animals have the specific purpose of producing motion, and in horses that includes running, jumping, bucking, and kicking. Colts love to get out and exercise their muscles by zipping around the pasture, rearing, dodging, and nipping at their mothers, then dashing off to join in more foal-time games. Older horses, just like older humans, aren't so interested in useless exertion of muscle power.

Muscles account for nearly 50 percent of the total body weight of a horse. Basically the horse's muscle system resembles that of a man in that it is directed by nerve stimulation and has the ability to contract and change shape.

There are three types of muscles. Voluntary muscles, which are most often attached to the bony lever areas of the horse's skeleton, cause movement by direct command from the horse's brain.

There are involuntary muscles that work without conscious direction of the brain. Involuntary muscles include those which digest food, contract the pupils of the eye, or function in breathing.

Finally, there is the cardiac or heart muscle, which is in a class by itself, although it is also an involuntary muscle.

Most voluntary muscles are in sets of two and act in direct opposition to one another. One muscle may be contracting or flexing while the other's effort is employed in straightening or holding.

Voluntary muscles, even with good conditioning, can only work for short periods of time before they become fatigued and require a rest. You will note that a horse at work will soon begin to drop his head and neck, the first sign that muscle fatigue has started. It is not long after the head and neck are lowered that the whole muscle system needs a rest. If the rest is not offered, there is very likely going to be some muscle damage.

Involuntary muscles, on the other hand, can work for hours without showing fatigue. The heart, or cardiac muscle, gains its required rest during the split-second interval between beats.

With horses, the portions of the muscle system that are most subject to injury are the tendons and ligaments of the legs.

Tendons are long narrow extensions of bulky muscle. Tendons serve the purpose of taking the action of bulky muscle across joints and in changes of direction. Tendons run across the horse's knee, for example, where the bulky muscle of the forearm would not fit nicely.

SKELETON OF HORSE

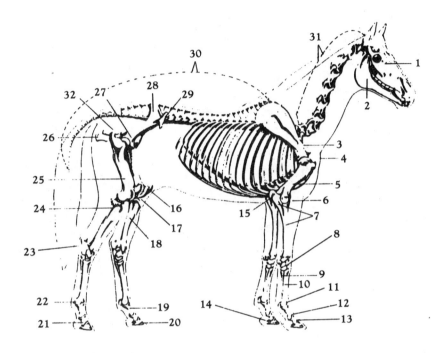

1. SKULL
2. MANDIBLE
3. SCAPULA (shoulder blade)
4. SHOULDER JOINT
5. HUMERUS (arm)
6. ELBOW JOINT
7. RADIUS AND ULNA (forearm)
8. CARPAL JOINT (knee)
9. 4th METACARPAL
   (outside splint bone)
10. 3rd METACARPAL
    (cannon bone)
11. FETLOCK JOINT
12. PASTERN JOINT
13. COFFIN JOINT
14. NAVICULAR BONE
15. POINT OF ELBOW

16. PATELLA (knee cap)
17. STIFLE JOINT
18. TIBIA
19. LONG PASTERN BONE
20. COFFIN BONE
21. SHORT PASTERN BONE
22. PROXIMAL SESAMOID BONES
23. TARSAL JOINT (hock)
24. FIBULA
25. FEMUR (thigh)
26. POINT OF BUTTOCK
27. PELVIS
28. POINT OF CROUP
29. POINT OF HIP
30. SPINOUS PROCESS
31. VERTEBRAE OF NECK
32. HIP JOINT

PARTS OF THE HORSE

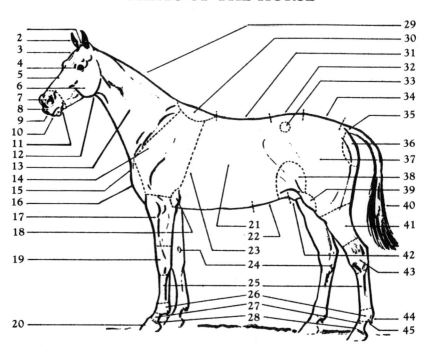

1. POLL	16. CHEST	31. BACK
2. EAR	17. FOREARM	32. LOIN
3. FOREHEAD	18. ELBOW	33. POINT OF HIP
4. EYE	19. KNEE	34. RUMP OR CROUP
5. FACE	20. HOOF	35. DOCK
6. CHEEK	21. BARREL	36. BUTTOCK
7. NOSTRIL	22. ABDOMEN	37. THIGH
8. MUZZLE	23. HEART GIRTH	38. FLANK
9. UPPER LIP	24. CHESTNUT	39. STIFLE
10. LOWER LIP	25. CANNON	40. TAIL
11. CHIN GROOVE	26. FETLOCK JOINT	41. GASKIN OR
12. THROATLATCH	27. PASTERN	SECOND THIGH
13. NECK	28. CORONET	42. SHEATH
14. SHOULDER	29. CREST	43. HOCK
15. POINT OF	30. WITHERS	44. FETLOCK
SHOULDER		45. ERGOT

Ligaments are inelastic, and primarily serve the function of holding joints in place. Ligaments around the fetlock joint, for example, allow the fetlock joint to have direct flexion, but prevent lateral or sideways movement.

Tendons and ligaments are frequently overstretched, strained, or torn away from the bone when the horse is overworked and tired, or when he twists in an unnatural movement.

Short, heavy muscle denotes quickness and power. This type of muscle is generally known as "fast twitch" muscle. It is great for a short burst of speed, but it burns a lot of oxygen and produces high amounts of waste, therefore is useful for only brief periods.

Longer, thin muscle, called "slow twitch" muscle, is much better for endurance, but doesn't produce the quick power of the heavier muscle.

A good combination of the two types of muscle produces a well-balanced and very versatile, athletic horse.

There's no secret to building muscle on a horse. It's done just as it is with humans: good diet, consistent work.

Unfortunately I can't send my horse to a body building gym. And, since he can't hold on to a barbell, I just let him carry a dumbbell.

What Is He Good For?

Horses are good for a lot of things. They are good to pet, and feed, and brush, and blanket. But, when you get right down to the nitty-gritty, they're best for "movin'."

When mankind first met the horse he thought the horse was good for "eatin'." But, he soon discovered he was best for movin'.

Horses and mankind have been doin' a lot of movin' together for the past 5,000 years, and yet, amazingly enough only a very small percentage of horsemen know how the horse moves. (Sure the muscles move the bones, but what we need to know now is how them bones gonna move about.)

Ask the average horseman, with five years experience, the sequence of strides at the walk, jog, or lope or the walk, trot, or canter and the average horseman won't know the answer. (As a matter of fact, the average horseman doesn't know the difference between a jog and a trot or a lope and a canter. The jog and the lope are western gaits, in which the flight of the foot travels a more rounded arc. Both gaits are somewhat unnatural and must be learned. The flight of the foot during the trot and the canter is much more natural and follows a longer, lower path.)

For some reason, even though the average horseowner has watched horses walk for years, they don't seem to know how they do it.

The most common error is thinking the horse starts walking by moving a front foot. He does not.

All of a horse's action initiates in the hindquarters.

The sequence of strides at the four-beat walk might be left hind, left fore, right hind, right fore. The front foot begins moving before the hind foot strikes the ground in its new position because a good horse overstrides his front foot print with his hind foot. If the horse doesn't overstride, he is said to be short behind — a good indication he may have a lameness.

The trot is a two-beat diagonal movement. The action is still initiated by the hindquarters, but in this case the diagonal front leg moves simultaneously. The horse may begin the trot by moving the right hind and left fore at the same time, then the left hind and the right fore.

There is no overstriding, and the horse must shorten his body and elevate the flight of the hoof. The jog is essentially a very short forward movement, while the trot should have good extention.

The lope or canter is a three-beat gait in which one side of the horse's body is extended (the leading side) and the other side is contracted. The contracting side does the pushing and the leading side does the landing.

The sequence for a left lead begins with the right hind foot, which takes a short stride. The left hind and the right fore then move together. The left hind is an extended stride while the right fore is a short stride.

The final beat is the left fore, which moves on a long stride.

Horses also pace, which means they move both legs on the same side at the same time.

In addition, some horses single-foot. A single-foot is a very smooth four-beat gait which could also be thought of as a very fast walk.

"Gaited" horses essentially walk, trot, and canter, but with very exaggerated and flashy foot flight. Most "gaited" horses maintain a flat back, which provides a very smooth ride.

The standard reply by horsemen who don't know the sequence of strides of a horse is, "So, what!"

So, the horse knows where his feet are supposed to go. When the rider doesn't, the horse is restricted, hindered, made to move incorrectly, is put under a strain, and can be injured. That's what!

When Ain't He Movin' Right?

The more we know, the more complicated things become.

It used to be a horse was lame or he wasn't.

Not so, today. Today the horse may or may not be "suitable for the purpose intended."

And most veterinarians don't perform "soundness" examinations anymore. Today they do "pre-purchase exams"; the result of which may be "suitable or unsuitable for the purpose intended." If the horse later goes lame, he was then probably worked in a manner not intended.

A horse is generally considered lame when pain or inability causes him to alter the usual weight distribution on one or more limbs, or exhibit abnormal extension or flexion of a joint during movement.

The detection of lameness can be easy, while the diagnosis of lameness is usually extremely complicated, unless the cause is evident in an open joint or wound.

If the average horseowner detects the lameness, that is usually sufficient. The veterinarian stands by with his special skills, drugs, and tools to make the diagnosis and plan treatment.

Slight lameness, especially in the hindquarters, is often best detected when the horse is in a stall. When turning his forehand from one side to the other, the horse with a spavin or stringhalt will shift his weight onto one hind leg more quickly than the other, which may be considered the unsound limb. If the lameness is in the forehand, the horse will be reluctant to shift his weight onto the affected limb.

A horse lame in the forehand will often "point" the affected limb. It is not uncommon for a horse to have one foot slightly advanced when standing quietly; however, if the horse is sound, both front feet will assume equal weight.

If the horse is "pointing," then the affected limb will be rested only on the toe, or heel, or if kept flat, will not bear weight. A horse lame in one front foot usually stands with its pastern straighter than with that of the sound one.

When examining a horse in movement, it is best to trot the horse. The trot is a diagonal two-beat gait at which only two feet are grounded at the same time, and therefore, each bears more weight than it would at the walk, in which three feet are grounded at the same time.

When a trotting horse is lame in a fore or hind leg, he will favor the unsound limb at the expense of its sound diagonal. If lame behind, he will often also appear lame in front since he will put more weight on the opposite foreleg from the unsound hind leg.

A lame horse will use his head and neck for balance to relieve the weight on the unsound limb. If lame in front, he will raise his head when the lame leg strikes the ground, bringing it more or less into normal position when the sound leg is grounded.

If the horse is lame behind, he will lower his head when the opposite foreleg is placed on the ground.

It takes a severe lameness to see a horse "nod" his head at the walk. The raising or lowering of the head is much more obvious at the trot, unless the handler is holding or pulling the head to one side, causing the horse mechanically to overload his weight on one side. Be sure the handler keeps the lead loose while trotting the horse.

If a horse is lame on both fore and hind legs, he will go short and stiff and lack freedom in placing his feet.

Sometimes it is best to take a rear view of the horse if it is thought he may be lame behind. If he is, the horse will "hitch up" the unsound quarter in an attempt to keep the weight off that side. Other signs of hindleg lameness are the dwelling on one foot longer than the other, or the higher lifting of one foot, or the dragging of a toe on the unsound foot.

Personally, I look at a horse and simply try to decide if he is "off" or "okay."

I like my horse either lame or not lame. If he's not lame, then I have nothing to worry about.

If he's lame, rather than suitable for the purpose intended, then I know where to start — call the veterinarian.

What Does One Do?

Television commercials show you what a horse does best.

"Here comes the king, here comes the big number one." And here come the Budweiser Clydesdales, 32 hoofs in action, feathers floating as each strikes the ground, and the rhythm of it and the sound — fantastic!

Or the Del Mar Race Course commercial. The starting gate bangs open and a burst of color and sleek muscle explodes forward; then a quick cut to the early morning swirls of fog and the Thoroughbreds and the pony horses splashing in the foaming Pacific surf.

Yes, television commercials show you what a horse does best. He strides, glides, prances, pulls, and jumps.

He's action, and he's beautiful; for every ounce of his being is "motion."

The horse put his motion to work for man first as a pack animal carrying baggage. Soon man had the horse pulling a travois, and then a chariot. As man improved on the design of the vehicles he wanted pulled, the horse improved too, getting bigger and stronger.

For years and years the horse was man's number one source of power for vehicles that ranged from fancy coaches to light gigs.

Justin Morgan was one of the great pullers of all time. He raced and won pulling a sulky. And, he won many, many weight pulling contests.

Today horses pull carts and buggies in horse shows, they pull logs in terrain unsuitable for machines, they pull drays in London, and they pull beer wagons and sleighs in television commercials.

Of course, man loves to ride the horse, and he loves it best when the horse moves smoothly. So, some horses "gait."

When the fastest means of transportation was by horseback, the most comfortable horses were those that ambled. The amble is a lateral two-beat gait the same as a pace, in which both feet on the same side of the horse move at the same time.

Today there is the Peruvian Paso, which is the only 100 percent naturally gaited horse. No devices are used to make him perform his extraordinarily smooth, four-beat gait.

Other gaited horses include the Tennessee Walker, the American Saddlebred, and the Missouri Fox Trotter.

Of all gaits, probably the most spectacular is the "rack." The rack is a very fast even gait in which each foot strikes the ground separately in quick succession. Over a straight course, a racking horse may cover a mile in 2 minutes, 20 seconds.

When there was no longer the need to ride a horse, then doing so became fun, sport, and art, and in any of the three categories the horse might prance.

Most frequently you'll see a horse prance in a parade. But, many refined and controlled "springy" movements might also be called prancing. Such action includes the passage, which is a slow prancing-like trot, or the piaffe, which is a prancing-trot in place.

The classic art of equitation (riding) is known as Haute Ecole, or high school. It is based on natural leaps and paces derived from tactics employed by cavalry in combat.

Brought to its highest form by the Spanish Riding School, the Lipizzaners (a breed of horse from Central Europe) perform the Airs Above the Ground. The most difficult and highly publicized is the "capriole." To perform the capriole, the horse must leap into the air, then kick out with both hind feet, and finally land on all four feet.

Exciting to watch and exciting to do is jumping. And horses do it well, although they really don't have the anatomy to jump vertically. Nonetheless, they do clear six feet with relative ease.

The official Federation Equestre Internationale record high jump was made in Santiago, Chile, in 1949 by the horse, Huasco, who cleared 8 feet 1¼ inches. The greatest jump ever recorded, however, was by Ben Bolt, who cleared 9 feet 6 inches at the Royal Horse Show in Sydney, Australia, in 1936.

But best of all, horses run.

For man, horse racing may be the Sport of Kings. For horses, it is a natural defense, and therefore, they have developed the talent well.

Some say the greatest race horse of all time was Man O'War, others say Secretariat, others argue for Exterminator.

I think the greatest race horse is the one I bet on, and he won, and paid $86.

Yes, you see what horses do best on television. You see them move.

But the greatest thrill is to pull or prance or jump or run — to move — with them.

A Horse of Another Color

There's always been a lot of argument about the color of horses, but it's just a matter of splitting hairs.

According to Dr. Ben K. Green, the recognized authority on the color of horses and author of a book about color that took 30 years to research, the color of a horse is determined by pigment patterns, not by pigment color.

To arrive at that conclusion, Dr. Green had to split a lot of hairs. He found that basically each horse had the same amount of pigment, but that each color had its own special pattern. Once he was able to recognize a particular pattern, he could tell the color of a horse by seeing only one hair.

Dr. Green says a horse hair is hollow and that the walls of the hair are clear. There is only one pigment color and that is amber, he adds.

"It is the pigment pattern and density which determines refraction of light, hence the shade of color to the human eye." Dr. Green claims you cannot predict the color of a foal. Nor, he says, has there ever been a breeding program more than 70 percent successful in producing colors the way genetic books say they should be produced.

Dr. Green lists the following as the colors of horses: dark bay, mahogany bay, standard bay, blood bay, light bay, standard brown, seal brown, black, gray, dun, liver chestnut, dark chestnut, standard chestnut, bright chestnut, dusty chestnut, light chestnut, sorrel, buckskin, copper dun, red roan, blue roan, rose gray, and grulla.

He says the only undesirable colors of a horse intended for use are the dilute colors, palomino, and claybank.

There's an old saying about white feet which should tell you something about the experience horsemen have had with color over the years. It goes like this: "One white foot, buy him; two white feet, try him; three white feet, deny him; four white feet, shoot him."

White on a horse does present problems, according to Dr. Green. He says white feet are worse to split, are softer, and should be shod if the horse is used constantly.

Of white on the hide, it is quicker to scald from sweat and heat than is a dark color, especially when the white is on the horse's face and around the eyes, he adds.

Other observations made by Dr. Green include the thought that the bay horse is the most durable, and that although cowboys brag about the dun and buckskin, you "rarely see fine breeding of a dun color."

The cowboy says the dun, buckskin, or grulla are the "toughest of horses," but Dr. Green believes they simply take better care of themselves.

"These colors," he says, "belong to horses of native, western breeding. There is very little hot blood infused and self-preservation and survival are more instinctive."

Dr. Green has observed sorrels and chestnuts have more action and more speed. But, he adds, they also have a more tender mouth. And the lighter shades of chestnut have weaker feet.

A gray's skin is exceptionally tough and can stand hard use, according to Dr. Green, while the palomino has the least durable skin.

And finally, contrary to popular belief, there are more bay and dark brown Arabians than there are gray Arabians.

Much of what this experienced veterinarian has to say about color will be argued for years to come. But he has studied carefully, and who better to talk of a horse in terms of color than a Dr. Green.

What a Horse Is Not

Next time you see a mule, keep in mind that but for the lack of a single chromosome and no homologous pairs, you might be looking at Secretariat.

You see, the difference between the horse and the mule is simply that the horse cells have a total number of 64 chromosomes, in 32 pairs that can be arranged in eight groups. The mule, however, has 63 chromosomes, not arranged in homologous (similar) pairs.

Had Secretariat had only 62 chromosomes, in 31 pairs, arranged in six groups, he would have been a donkey.

Frankly, I didn't know that myself. But Tom Constantino, editor-publisher of *Mr. Longears*, the official publication of the American Donkey and Mule Society, Inc., does know of such things.

To understand more about the mule, the hinny, the donkey, or the burro, remember that *Equus asinus* is an ass (or, more commonly, a donkey or burro) and *Equus caballus* is a horse.

And that when you cross a male ass (jack) with a female horse, you get a mule. But when you cross a male horse with a female ass (jenny), you get a hinny.

The mule and the hinny supposedly cannot reproduce, although there are recorded cases of Molly mules having foals. Constantino says the exact mechanism involved in the maintenance of sterility by hybrid mammals has not yet been completely demonstrated, as undoubtedly there are many factors involved.

An interesting legend accompanies the cross that appears on the back of many donkeys and mules. It is said the donkey colt ridden into Jerusalem by Jesus Christ followed him to his crucifixion, and the sun's casting the shadow of the cross onto the donkey's back made a permanent mark, to be noted on the donkey forevermore. The cross on a donkey's back is noted in written works appearing only after Christ's crucifixion.

The great work mules so popular in America during the late 1700s and early 1800s contributed significantly to our agricultural success. Standing as high as 17 hands, these mules were kept as riding animals and pets, as well as for pulling plows and wagons.

George Washington was not only the first president of the United States, but he was also the first recorded breeder of mammoth mules in this country. He had a great faith in the draft mule, and said on many occasions, "The mule is essential for America's future development." And he was not speaking of politicians.

President Washington had a number of huge jacks standing at stud at Mount Vernon, but his favorite was probably Royal Gift, a large, black Catalan ass presented to him as a gift from the Spanish throne.

So next time you see a mule, remember, a horse he is not; he's a creature all his own.

2

Can a Horse's Dogs Bark?

Some things are so true you get sick of hearing them.

Such as, "I told you so."

Or, "Where there's smoke, there's fire."

The truest thing you can say about a horse is, "No hoof, no horse."

It's so true that 9 times out of 10 when a horse goes lame the problem is in a hoof. And the one time it isn't, a hoof was probably a contributing cause.

A horse's hoof — if you stretch the comparison — is the same as a the fingernail of a person's middle finger. The thumb and the little finger were long ago transformed into the ergot and the chestnut.

The index finger and the third finger are the "splint" bones.

Now the horse's hoof has an interesting configuration, serves an elaborate function, and, surprisingly, has a lot of moving parts.

As the hoof hits the ground, preferably flat because the foot is balanced and naturally shaped, the quarters expand outward. At the same time, the digital cushion expands, pressing against the lateral cartilages, further spreading the quarters.

At this point the short pastern bone presses the cushion down against the frog and the frog moves downward toward the ground.

When the hoof hits the ground, a direct compressive force is exerted upward through the multiple horn tubules, spring-like spirals in the hoof wall.

The hoof wall is connected to the coffin bone inside the foot by an interlocking of insensitive and sensitive laminae. It is sensitive laminae that attach to the coffin bone.

The narrow but strong hoof wall absorbs the upward force created when the hoof hits the ground, and the frog, digital cushion, coffin bone, and laminae absorb the downward force of the horse's body weight — compressive force.

As complicated as that may seem, it works quite well if the hoof is healthy, in balance, pliable, yet strong.

Some common hoof problems are corns, thrush, cracks, seedy toe, and gravel.

Corns are a bruising of the sole in the area of the hoof bar. Such bruising generally occurs because the hoofs were not trimmed or shod on a regular basis, or because the shoes were improperly fitted.

Most good horsemen agree a pleasure or show horse should be trimmed or shod approximately each 30 days. The maximum length of time between trims or shoeing should normally never exceed six weeks.

Thrush is a bacterial infection that thrives in nonaerated environments. It is prevented by proper daily cleaning of the hoof.

Hoof cracks are simply cracks in the wall of the hoof and are called "quarter cracks" if they are in the area of the quarters, or "toe cracks" if they are at the toe.

The cracks may begin at the coronet or at the weight-bearing edge. On occasion they extend the entire length of the hoof wall.

The most frequent cause of cracks is a loss of wall elasticity due to a lack of moisture. (The healthy hoof is essentially 50 percent liquid.)

A cracked heel is a lesion just below the hair at the back of the fetlock. Such cracks usually excrete pus. Scabs can form, then break and bleed.

Cracked heel is the result of unsanitary conditions. It can affect one or more hoofs, and it can spread to other horses.

If cracked heel becomes severe the horse's entire leg can swell.

Seedy toe is a separation of the hoof wall from the sole. It is often caused by chronic laminitis.

Proper trimming, and avoidance of a long toe will usually correct the situation.

Gravel is an infection that gains entrance to the hoof through the bottom, particularly near or at the junction of the wall and sole.

Such infection will generally make the horse lame, and lameness will continue until the infection works its way upward through the hoof, eventually breaking out at the coronary band.

When a horse suffers from any of the above-mentioned maladies, boy do his dogs bark — fourfold!

Rules to Stand On

I ask: Upon what will the future of the horse stand, if not upon the hoof?

And the answer comes back, "I was going to take care of his feet last week, but I forgot."

We're breeding horses with feet too small for their size and weight.

We worry about the horse's coat, but seldom expend effort on the hoof. And when we do, it's often a dab of hoof polish to cover past sins.

And we shoe too soon, often for the wrong reasons, and most of the time, improperly.

Worst of all, because it's the underlying cause of the other problems, is the fact that the average horseowner doesn't understand the horse's hoof.

The exterior parts of the hoof include the wall, the sole, the bars, the heel, and the frog. The normal, healthy foot is strong, smooth, and well-balanced. Front feet are larger, rounder, and stronger than hind feet since they carry more of the horse's total weight; while the shape of the hind feet best suits the function of driving the horse.

Any ridges, rings, cracks, or an unbalanced shape should be considered unhealthy and abnormal.

The wall, or exterior surface of the hoof, is hard. It covers the highly sensitive interior parts of the foot and protects them from injury. These parts include the bones, laminae, plantar cushion, various tendons and ligaments, blood vessels, and nerves. The wall has the greatest ground contact and supports most of the horse's weight.

The wall continually grows down from the coronary band, and excess growth must be removed. The healthy hoof grows three-eighths to one-half inch per month.

The sole of the foot is a fairly soft, shelly growth and should be concave. The sole and the frog of the foot do not grow indefinitely, but naturally discard excessive flakes or scales once they reach their natural thickness.

The bars of the foot are actually extensions of the wall, acting as a brace to keep the foot from overexpansion as weight is placed upon it.

The heel is very sensitive, with only thin wall protection, and should be constantly checked for it is subject to painful ground burns or bruises.

The frog is the "V" shaped elastic substance, with its wide base at the heel and its apex at the center of the hoof.

DIAGRAM OF THE HORSE'S HOOF

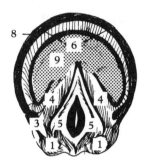

Normal Forefoot

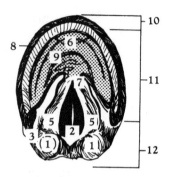

Normal Hind foot

1. BULBS
2. CENTRAL SULCUS
   OF FROG (spine/stay)
3. ANGLE OF WALL
4. BARS
5. COLLATERAL
   SULCUS

6. WHITE LINE
7. APEX OF FROG
8. WALL
9. SOLE
10. TOE
11. QUARTER
12. HEEL

1. SKIN
2. TENDON OF COMMON
   EXTENSOR
3. METACARPAL BONE
4. FIRST PHALANX
5. SECOND PHALANX
6. COFFIN BONE
7. DISTAL SESAMOID
   BONE
8. CAPSULE OF
   FETLOCK JOINT
9. FETLOCK JOINT
10. PASTERN JOINT
11. SOLE
12. CORIUM OF SOLE
13. FROG
14. DIGITAL CUSHION
15. DEEP FLEXOR TENDON
16. CORONARY CORIUM
17. PERIOPLE
18. MIDDLE SESAMOID
    LIGAMENT
19. SUPERFICIAL SESAMOID
    LIGAMENT
20. ERGOT

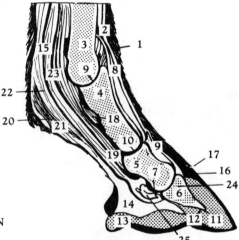

21. FIBROUS TISSUE
22. SUPERFICIAL FLEXOR
    TENDON
23. INTERSESAMOID LIGAMENT
24. COFFIN JOINT
25. NAVICULAR BONE

Inside the healthy and properly shaped hoof, the major bones and ligaments are adjusted and balanced in such a way that there are no unequal strains.

Everything is harmony, until something gets out of balance through a lack of care or improper care.

And, that's when baby needs new shoes. (Usually baby needs new shoes or trimming about every 30 days, and no less than every six weeks.)

Regardless of what you may have heard, poor shoeing is very common, and a most frequent contributor to lameness.

Long toes and low heels are the single greatest errors made by farriers. Neither is desirable. Don't allow either.

The angulation of the hoof should not be an exact 45 degrees as is so often quoted. The angulation should be what is natural for the horse. The proper angulation is found by keeping the hoof wall at the toe parallel with the shoulder at the crest of the withers. This angle should also have the hoof wall parallel with the long pastern bone.

An easy, close check on the proper angulation can be made by dropping a line down the center of the cannon bone. The line should touch the back of the heel at ground surface.

The shoer should never try to straighten the horse's legs by changing the hoof. The hoof should strike the ground flat no matter how crooked the leg appears to be.

Generally the hoof should be rasped at the toe to reduce toewall thickness.

The sole should be pared out slightly to maintain it's natural concave form.

The frog should be pared down to allow for compression expansion. It has been erroneously written for years that the frog should touch the ground. Don't you believe it.

When the frog is left so deep it hits the ground at the same time as the hoof wall, it feels for the horse much as it feels for you when the horse puts his hoof on your toe.

Thrush Is a Dirty Bird

In the world of horses, thrush is not a songbird.

It's a dirty bird.

Thrush is an unhealthy condition of the feet, which is most frequently blamed on dirty stalls. It ought to be blamed on horseowners.

It's true that unsanitary conditions are mainly the cause of thrush, but a lack of proper exercise can also be responsible, as can poor foot care, particularly infrequent cleaning and improper trimming of the wall, sole, and frog.

The sole and frog produce excessive growth after they reach a sufficient thickness to protect the foot. This dead matter must be removed by the farrier so the living sole and frog are clean.

Thrush loves to attack the neglected foot or the foot that is packed with manure and mud.

Thrush is characterized by a very offensive odor.

And in especially bad cases, thrush produces a dark, smelly fluid similar to dirty crankcase oil.

Thrush is caused by a bacterium, *Fusobacterium*, found everywhere, but preferring damp, wet, or marshy areas. Dirty stall bedding is an ideal breeding ground.

Naturally, horses left in stalls or small corrals suffer from thrush more frequently than horses at pasture. But as the winter months approach and the rains come, pastured horses whose feet are not cared for regularly will also become victims.

If the horseman notices the offensive odor of thrush when he is cleaning the horse's feet, it's a pretty good sign additional foot care is needed.

In mild cases, thrush rarely causes lameness and is relatively easy to treat. However, in severe cases, where discharge in the crevices around the frog is evident, lameness can develop. Thrush lameness is difficult to cure, difficult to treat, and requires the services of a veterinarian.

Often thrush is a spin-off disease created by another lameness. If the horse has thrush in just one foot or both front feet, then lameness from another source should be considered even if it isn't yet observable.

Prevention of thrush, of course, is the best cure.

The horse's feet should be cleaned thoroughly daily. It takes only a moment or two and is not asking too much of the thoughtful or concerned owner. The horse's feet must always be cleaned before he is worked.

If thrush develops, trim away the infected portions of the frog, and be sure to clean the crevices between the frog and sole deeply. As soon as the foot has been cleaned, you can pour a household bleach into the crevices, making sure the bleach does not slop over onto the heel or the coronary band.

Tincture of iodine or a commercially produced medication can also be applied to the diseased frog.

An old-time remedy for thrush is a poultice of boiled turnips to which a few drops of carbolic acid or powdered charcoal have been added. The poultice should be kept on the foot for two or three days.

Stalls, corrals, or paddocks should be cleaned frequently and fresh bedding should be supplied regularly. Check stall drainage so pools of urine or water do not collect.

Good, consistent exercise keeps the foot healthy and is an excellent preventive measure.

Do not let the horse go longer than six weeks between shoeing or trimming.

Without thrush, your horse will sing a happy song.

Founder Is Not Sounder

When most people talk of founder they are referring to something bad, which it is; something caused by eating too much grain, which it can be; and something not often seen, which is wrong.

Founder is an old name. The more modern name is laminitis, which means there is an inflammation of the laminae of the foot. The inflammation may be caused by infectious or noninfectious agents.

Both the causes and the treatment of laminitis are still very much under study, and there is still a great deal of disagreement about the condition.

"What we know for sure," says Dr. John W. Byrd, D.V.M., "is laminitis is a much more common phenomenon than most horsemen previously believed."

Laminitis can affect both front feet, which is common, or all four feet. If all four feet are affected, the horse will tend to lie down for extended periods. If only the front feet are affected, the horse will extend the front legs to stand essentially on his heels in an effort to eliminate weight from the feet.

Heat is present in the sole, wall, and coronary band, says Dr. Byrd. The arteries that run down the pasterns throb, and tapping the hoof even lightly causes pain.

The horse with laminitis suffers great distress and is unwilling to move.

Grain founder is the most well known and is probably the most common, says Dr. Byrd. Ingestion of greater quantities of grain than can be tolerated is the cause. Such founder is often accidental, such as a horse getting to an open grain bin.

A horse can founder when he drinks large amounts of cold water immediately after he has become overheated.

Grass founder is common among horses that are grazed on summer pastures, especially if the pastures contain clover and alfalfa.

When overweight horses are turned out in lush grass pastures, the result is frequently founder.

Ponies are especially susceptible to founder, Dr. Byrd says.

Lack of sufficient exercise is another cause, which is possibly becoming much more frequent. Horses left in box stalls for long periods then taken out and worked are good candidates. This may be a similar founder to what was known as road founder, the result of concussion to the feet from hard or fast work on a hard surface. Unconditioned horses are especially subject to such founder.

Once the horse has suffered from laminitis, there are usually heat rings around the hoof wall, and the hoof, over a period of time, tends to curl up at the toe.

In a severe case there is often a "dropping" of the sole and a "rotation" of the coffin bone, says Dr. Byrd.

In any case of laminitis the prognosis is always guarded. If the symptoms continue for more than 10 days, the future for the horse is unfavorable, Dr. Byrd warns, especially in the case of rotation of the coffin bone, which is revealed by radiographs.

The signs of founder are quite obvious, and a veterinarian should be called *immediately*. The quicker aid is given, the better the chances of reducing the damage.

Depending on the type of founder, the veterinarian will formulate a treatment. While waiting for the vet, the horseowner may wish to stand the horse in cold water. This may or may not help, but it won't hurt.

At the vet's direction, assistance from a farrier may eventually get the horse suitable for work. Frequent hoof trims, the use of a wide web shoe or leather or rubber pads, or an egg-bar shoe may be recommended.

In any case, founder is not a problem to be taken lightly. While it isn't often fatal, it can quickly render a horse useless.

And, founder is much more common than the average horseowner believes.

Commonly "Unwanted"

Ringbone and sidebone are two nasty conditions seen rather frequently in backyard or pleasure riding horses, but not generally common among top show or racing stock.

Both conditions are associated with poor conformation and, therefore, don't appear as often in horses selected for their correctness of form, or athletic abilities.

Ringbone is nothing more than new bone growth on or at the joints of the first, second, or third phalanges. The conformation of the horse may tend to encourage a binding force on the joints of the coffin and pastern bones. A failure to keep the horse's hoofs trimmed regularly, or improper trimming with a long toe and short heel, results in stress on the front of the pastern and coffin joints. Such unrelieved pressure or even some type of external trauma may initiate new bone growth.

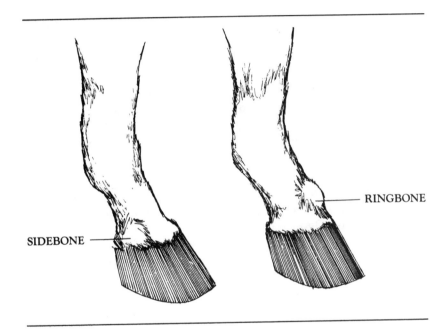

SIDEBONE

RINGBONE

The new bone growth, Dr. Byrd explains, is the response of damaged bone tissue.

The lameness, whether from high (pastern joint) or low (coffin joint) ringbone, results from the irritation caused by the new bone growth.

In a few cases there will be little or no lameness with ringbone. However, says Dr. Byrd, when there is lameness it is usually evident at any gait, but is most pronounced when the horse is trotted in a circle.

There is often inflammation involved and an obvious enlargement on the front of the pastern. Ringbone can affect both front and hind feet, but is most common in front.

The treatment, says Dr. Byrd, usually involves therapy to reduce the inflammation caused by the ringbone. Anti-inflammatory drug therapy and corrective shoeing are used with some success.

Sidebone is an ossification of the lateral cartilage and appears as a hard, bone-like bump above the bulb of the heel. Sidebone can be inside, outside, and on one or both front feet.

Normally, if you press your thumb against the bulb of the heel it has a springy feeling. When sidebone is present, the area will be hard and immovable, observes Dr. Byrd.

There are probably three causes of sidebone.

Trauma to the area, Dr. Byrd says, is one possibility, but the less likely.

Poor conformation, especially a toe-in or toe-out, is common with sidebone.

Poor shoeing that gives the foot an improper angulation and makes it unlevel is frequently a cause of sidebone, according to Dr. Byrd.

With poor conformation or poor shoeing there is an unequal stress on the foot. One result can be the ossification of the lateral cartilage.

"Rarely does sidebone cause lameness," states Dr. Byrd. "The lameness generally follows a fracture of the sidebone. In other words, an enlargement of bone is produced, then it fractures, and the broken segment moves and causes pain."

Sidebone may be effectively treated by preparing special shoes for the horse. "What we must accomplish," says Dr. Byrd, "is the elimination of pressure to the injured area."

If corrective shoeing isn't the answer, a neurectomy (heel nerving) may be the only solution.

"Once it has been established that sidebone is the cause of lameness, heel nerving is a viable option to the horseowner," Dr. Byrd says. "I've had very good success with neurectomies. Many horses have been used for years after heel nerving, free of pain."

Both ringbone and sidebone can easily be seen in radiographs, and both should be attended by a veterinarian.

The Disease That Isn't

Navicular disease isn't, but what it is is probably much more common and afflicts many more horses than most horsemen would guess.

Navicular diease is a misnomer. We don't have a Black Plague. Actually what we have, when we have an inflammation, or bruise, or adhesions between the navicular bone and the deep flexor tendon, is a "navicular condition," according to Dr. Byrd.

"And, a navicular condition is one of the major causes of lameness in horses," Dr. Byrd affirms.

Navicular problems are not always diagnosed early, says Dr. Byrd, because frequently the lameness clears up when the horse is given a bit of rest; or the lameness is thought to be in the shoulders; or, if radiographs are taken, there are no significant changes seen in the navicular bone.

Dr. Byrd believes one of the principal causes of navicular conditions is poor shoeing. It has become quite common today for the horse's heels to be cut quite low, and the toes to be left long. The effect is to break the pastern bones back, causing the deep flexor tendon, which runs across the navicular bone, to assume an unnatural strain.

The insidious nature of this situation, says Dr. Byrd, is that the navicular bone and the deep flexor tendon get no relief, even when the horse is standing quietly in his stall. So, a navicular condition may develop over a period of time, even though the horse may appear perfectly at ease.

"I suspect," says Dr. Byrd, "that such circumstances are a far greater contributor to navicular lameness than had been previously estimated."

Navicular condition has been attributed to many causes, says Dr. Byrd: genetic predisposition, conformation, improper shoeing, type of work performed, nutrition, and the breeding of large horses with small feet.

According to Dr. Byrd, horses suffering a navicular condition may demonstrate an unnatural gait. If the horse appears to be tiptoeing across eggs while at work, a trainer or rider has reason to suspect a navicular condition.

Once the condition has progressed, the horse will usually show lameness after working, then get better with rest. Once put back to work, the lameness will return.

During movement, the horse will tend to land on the toe of the foot to avoid concussion to the heel area. Usually, the condition is found in both front feet. The signs of lameness often shift from one front foot to the other. (Navicular lamenesses are seldom discovered in hind feet.)

A veterinarian can frequently determine a navicular condition with the aid of hoof testers, which are used like pliers to apply pressure to the foot. Although, in the early stages, radiographs will not often show significant navicular bone changes, a nerve block will usually aid in diagnosing a navicular condition.

According to Dr. Byrd, while the prognosis is not favorable in most cases, there is a lot which can be done to help the horse.

"If caught early enough, corrective shoeing techniques and special shoes can help the horse," Dr. Byrd says.

Primarily what is required, he says, is the restoration of the hoof to its natural shape and balance. Drug therapy is used to reduce inflammation.

If the condition is severe and chronic, then it is possible to salvage a number of useful years of service from the horse by performing a neurectomy (heel nerving).

As a result of heel nerving, there are many horses who are enjoying life again without the pains of a navicular condition.

3

He's Got Senses, and a Vocabulary Too!

Humans need to communicate, and horses need to communicate, and horses and humans need to communicate.

Communication is the basis for all horsemanship. When messages get mixed up, or misunderstood, the horse doesn't react in the manner desired by the human. When the message is understood, the horse reacts as desired, and harmony exists.

The human, who is supposedly of superior intelligence, always expects the horse to understand the human's message. You infrequently hear a human say, "I apparently was not clear in my request."

Why is it the one of supposedly superior intelligence always expects the one of supposedly less intelligence to do all the work of learning?

The really intelligent horseman doesn't expect the horse to learn his language, without the horseman first learning the horse's language.

Researchers estimate the horse's vocabulary at 47 basic messages with 30 variations of inflections, or a total of 1,410 communicative expressions.

Ah, but the horse uses his eyes, ears, nostrils, tail, muscles, and voice to deliver his messages.

A horse's nostrils quiver, expand, and contract to register interest, suspicion, fear, or temper.

A horse's tail is an indicator of his health or state of mind. To show elation, the tail is held nearly parallel to the spine. Exhaustion is signaled by a quivering tail, and a switching tail indicates fear or pain. If the horse clamps the tail tightly down, he is being asked to approach something that terrifies him.

It is interesting to note that, according to the experts, if a stallion is used exclusively for breeding, his vocabulary is limited pretty much to enthusiastic and noisy outbursts at the sight of a mare. However, if the stallion is put to work, his vocabulary generally expands rapidly.

Experts on horse vocabulary agree a stallion used under saddle seems to have more winning ways with broodmares as a result of his enlarged vocabulary. (That apparently holds true for humans too, as the macho man is initially exciting to women, but generally loses to the more stable competitor.)

It has been proved that when a horse realizes you are trying to understand what he is saying to you, his vocabulary will increase, sometimes double. The horse will make a genuine effort to communicate with you. He will be a good listener, if you keep his interest.

Instincts Result in Behavior

There is absolutely no doubt in my mind that of every 1,000 horses, 999 are smarter than the person riding them.

We give horses credit for having the mentality of a 3-year-old child. We don't give them enough credit for being "consistent and reasonable."

Most riders are over the age of three, yet they seldom if ever are reasonable. They *are* consistent — blaming everything on the horse, failing to understand, and demonstrating their own low mental capacity by resorting to force and violence.

Genuine communication is possible only through a knowledge of the horse's mental processes, which are, in order of importance: herd instinct, need for security, the following instinct, love of routine, laziness, excitability and nervousness, sensitivity, and courage.

Even though most horses don't live in a herd today, it is the companionship instinct that is strongest. Untrained and young horses are most reluctant to leave a group. When the training process begins they are frequently forced to do just that, and the trouble begins.

The instinct, however, can be exploited, and is by the intelligent trainer. Young horses are accompanied by an older, trained horse. Training areas by design are close enough to home (the stall or corral) to be familiar, but are far enough away from a group of horses so as not to be distracting. Young horses are allowed to watch companions perform prior to being asked for the same exercise — such as crossing water or jumping. Horses being schooled are worked toward their friends, rather than away from the group.

As the horse learns to respect and trust the handler, the horse will become more secure and, therefore, more calm — a prerequisite to training.

The following instinct is of great advantage to the trainer-rider, if the knowledge is put to use.

Most horses have a natural inclination to obey, which makes them surprisingly cooperative. But this is a double-edged sword. If the handler knows what he is asking, and is consistent in doing so, the horse will eventually perform exercises as they were designed. If the handler doesn't know what he is asking, the horse will still eventually perform as requested, by running away, throwing his head, stopping at jumps, etc.

By dominating the horse, consistently and reasonably, instead of employing cutesy, lovey nonsense, the handler is filling a basic need in the horse, and the horse responds.

The love of routine is basic to the horse's security, calm, and well-being, just as it is basic to training methods. Good trainers map out a program of progress for the horse, repeating basic steps and building upon them. The poor horseman jumps from one exercise to another, never establishing anything, except frustration.

The love of routine is linked to the horse's natural laziness and, understanding that, it is foolish of a rider to ask more of a horse than is required. If a horse gets an exercise correct, and demonstrates he understands the rider's request, why keep asking the horse to do it over and over again until he is exhausted?

Horses are also excitable and nervous, traits that in years past helped them to avoid predators. The horse's nervous system is highly tuned, and shouting at or abusing a frightened horse only makes matters worse.

Linked to excitability and nervousness is the great sensitivity of the horse, without which it would be impossible to achieve subtle cues. Knowing of the horse's sensitivity, the good trainer always begins with a minimal cue, never with a forceful one.

The most useful attribute of the horse's mind is his extraordinary memory. Put in the correct things and you get the correct response. Put in anything else and that's what you get back.

For the memory to work well, however, cause and effect, reward and punishment must be closely related in time. Don't wait to praise the horse when he does something well, or to punish the horse that knows better, but has refused to comply.

The horse's great courage is demonstrated by his repeated, and often thwarted, attempts to trust man.

They say it's horse sense which keeps horses from betting on humans. I agree.

It's knowing that a horse has sense that keeps me betting on the horse 999 times out of 1,000.

Ears to Hear and Hold

Having something in your ear not only keeps you from hearing well, it's also uncomfortable and makes you extremely irritable.

Compared to other animals, horses rarely have trouble with their ears, which play an important role in just about everything a horse does. He listens with his ears and hears very well. He also talks with his ears, pointing out activities that interest him.

Watch a horse's ears for a few minutes, and you'll notice they are rarely still. They're up, they're down, they're sideways. Always they're active.

So, if you think ear troubles are a problem for you, speculate on how much trouble an ear problem is for a horse.

One of the most common discomforts a horse suffers is infestation by ear ticks. These parasites invade the ear canal, becoming extremely irritating. The horse will shake his head, but to no avail. He'll lay the ears back and he'll resent anyone touching the ear.

There's no way you're going to get the ear ticks out, so call a veterinarian. The vet will provide a medication to kill the ear ticks.

Wax buildup in the ear is also very uncomfortable for the horse. Ear wax can be dissolved with cerumenolytic agents, which can be provided by your veterinarian.

A lot of horses get flat, gray warts in their ears. These are persistent, but usually don't bother the horse too much. Treatment for such warts is usually not recommended. (In most cases these warts are more troublesome to the horse's owner than they are to the horse.)

There are other tumors that invade the horse's ear. Sarcoids are relatively common, as are meanoma on or in the ears of gray horses.

The tips of the ears are often frozen off horses that are pastured in extremely cold areas. Foals born in the high country often lose the tips of the ears due to frostbite. The tips of the ears are generally the last part of the new foal to dry and are, therefore, susceptible to the cold.

And the ears are very subject to wounds. Split-eared horses are a pretty common sight. Such splits can usually be repaired with cosmetic surgery. Even splits several years old can be repaired by a skilled vet.

There are several conditions that do not involve the ear itself, but which may affect the horse's ear.

Parotitis is swelling and inflammation of the parotid salivary gland, just below the ear. With parotitis, the horse isn't going to like you fooling with his ear.

Diseases of the guttural pouch can also cause a swelling beneath the ear. The guttural pouch is peculiar to the horse. It is a sac that opens into the eustachian tube of the inner ear. It can become infected; sometimes with foals it distends with air, causing a condition known as tympanitis.

Tympanitis and parotitis both need the attention of a veterinarian.

"Sour ears" is a condition having nothing to do with disease. It's the symptom of a horse that doesn't like his companions, his rider, or his work. The sour-eared horse lays his ears flat back on his head just because he's unhappy, not because he has an ear problem.

Mistakenly a lot of people claim "earing" a horse will make the horse ear-shy. If done properly, "earing" is a satisfactory method of restraint that will leave the horse with no ill effects.

Attacking a horse's ear suddenly, or trying to pull the ear off, will make a horse ear-shy.

But, if the ear is grasped gently, then intermittent and powerful pressure is applied with the fingertips, and finally the ear is released gently, the horse will show no signs of "shyness."

Good Lookers Are Smart

Horses have remarkable eyes. They can, at one time or another, and sometimes in combination, have a feather in the eye, a glass eye, a pig eye, a pop eye, a smoky eye, or a walleye.

In addition, they have both monocular and binocular vision. The horse uses monocular vision to view separate things with each eye at the same time. These objects are to the side and rear of the horse. Binocular vision, for the horse, is frontal vision, and for it the horse concentrates both eyes on the same object.

The horse can see to the front, the side, and the rear. In fact, he has a field of vision of up to 300 degrees.

But his wide-angle vision may adversely influence his ability to learn or the level of his intelligence, or both.

Large eyes, set well out to the side of the head have always been considered a mark of quality in the horse. And while the horse should have large eyes, having the eyes placed well out to the side may be a handicap for the horse — from a learning point of view.

The farther out the eyes are placed on the side of the head, the more the horse must concentrate to achieve frontal vision.

Distractions limit his ability to concentrate, which in turn makes him slower to learn or, as some might say, less intelligent. On learning ability scales, animals that have just frontal vision generally rate higher than animals with monocular vision.

But this is only one of the horse's vision-related limitations.

We are pretty sure the horse does not see in color. And we know the retina of the horse's eye is somewhat flattened rather than curved. This means objects are quite frequently out of focus. To bring them into focus, horse must lower, tilt, or raise his head.

The horse's eye does not focus well on objects that are closer than four feet, and when a horse has his head high in the air, he cannot see the ground in front of him. Because of a special system within his eye, which absorbs light rays from above, the horse cannot see clearly that which is above the level of his eyes.

And while the horse has a wide field of vision, he does have two blind spots. They are close to his face, directly in front of him; and the width of his body, directly behind him. These blind spots are the cause of many problems for both horse and man.

All the special advantages and limitations of the horse's vision have a great deal to do with the way the horse behaves.

Just imagine what a young horse sees the first time he is taken on a trail ride or to a horse show!

There is the excitement of a strange place, cars, motorcycles, people, noises, and all sorts of unknown objects. Moreover, at any one time there is always something happening on each side of the horse. In many cases, the action isn't in focus, and even if it were , the horse wouldn't understand it. To see what is going on in front of him, the horse must concentrate his full attention straight ahead, but how can he do that when there is so much new and interesting to see on each side of him?

Seeing is certainly disbelieving for the young horse. He must be asking himself, "How could my master put me in such an incomprehensible world?"

Can you blame him for being a little flighty?

Most of us do and, consequently, try to jerk, spank, or force the horse into being calm when he is upset by being introduced to the unfamiliar.

It won't work. Only understanding how the horse sees will help.

And then there is terminology, such as "a feather in his eye." A feather refers to a visible blemish on the eye. The blemish may be the result of an injury or a natural defect. In either case, it is considered a fault.

A glass eye lacks color and may be the cause for disqualification by some breed registries. A pig eye is a small squinty eye, and a horse that has pig eyes is generally considered stubborn and hard to handle.

A pop eye is the opposite of a pig eye; it is the description given to an eye that seems to be too large and protruding from the head. A smoky eye is an eye that is cloudy in color, almost smoke gray. A walleye is another term for an eye without color and is sometimes referred to as a China eye.

Skin Deep

He feels the softest of caresses. He feels the pressure of a lower leg. He feels the sting of a whip.

He also feels the discomfort of an itch, sunburn, and a variety of rashes.

All this feeling a horse does with his skin — a part of him we seldom see. We see the glossy sleekness of a velvety coat, but we don't often see the superficial nonvascular (without blood vessels) layer, the cuticle, or epidermis. And, unless we are looking at a major wound, we never see the deep vascular (with blood vessels) layer, the corium, dermis, or true skin.

And we practically never think of the fact there is an intimate nervous sympathy of different points of the skin with particular internal organs.

In the horse, as well as in man, certain skin disorders can be causative of internal disease, and certain internal diseases causative of affections of the skin.

A skin eruption often follows certain disorders of the stomach, the liver, the kidneys, or even the lungs. A simple burn of the skin can cause inflammations of internal organs, and inflammation of such organs can, in their turn, cause eruptions on the skin.

A visible disorder in the skin of a horse may point to a particular fault in diet, to an injudicious use of cold water when the horse was overheated, to a fault in the stable's drainage, ventilation, or lighting.

When a horse is suffering from strange lumps or bumps on his skin, don't just assume they are mosquitoe bites and ignore them. It could be an internal problem.

Or, they could be parasitic skin diseases caused by flies, leeches, lice, ticks, poultry mites, mange, or ringworm.

On the other hand, it could be simple eczema.

Or, it could be an allergic reaction to fly sprays, the use of certain drugs, or a fungus.

Skin problems caused by allergies can also be accompanied by swelling around the eyes, swelling of head and legs, labored breathing, an increased heart rate, and sometimes a sticky serum on the skin.

The best treatment for an allergy is, of course, to remove the thing to which the horse is allergic. If you can't determine the cause of the external skin reaction, then give the horse a little time, and he'll probably build up an immunity and the lumps or bumps will go away.

If the horse is in discomfort, and the allergy symptoms are pronounced, call a veterinarian. The vet may not know the cause, but can at least treat the symptoms, providing immediate relief from the itch or pain.

Biting flies cause a horse a lot of skin problems. Many horses are so sensitive to fly bites, especially on the legs, they suffer from scabby sores and bleeding.

The best method I've found for eliminating this problem is to have the horse wear socks during the worst of the fly season. A pair of athletic socks, with the toes cut out, slip easily over the horse's legs and stay in place nicely.

Horses with a lot of white on their heads, especially around the eyes and muzzle, are subject to severe sunburn. A little dab of zinc oxide ointment will help relieve the pain and prevent further burning. The most effective prevention technique is to keep the horse from playing too long around the pool or on the beach.

Some horses are pretty thick-skinned, and it really doesn't matter what you say about them. They ignore all derogatory comments. Others are a little thin-skinned, and you have to be careful what you say, or you might hurt their feelings.

In either case, you must remember, beauty is only skin deep, so take care of your horse's skin.

You know how vain he is!

Open Wide

I don't think the majority of horses like the dentist any more than we do. But, just the same, they need regular checkups. At least twice a year.

Even though they don't brush after every meal, they'll seldom have a cavity — just a few rough edges.

The rough edges develop because the horse's upper jaw is wider than the lower jaw. Therefore, the outside edge of the upper molars and the inside edge of the lower molars are not worn smooth during the grinding process of chewing. These sharp edges can cut the inside of the horse's mouth and make him most uncomfortable.

To smooth out the situation, and get the horse chewing properly again, the veterinarian will "float" the horse's teeth. Water isn't used to do the job; a long-handled rasp, known as a "float," is used.

Horses frequently object to having their teeth filed, but not because it hurts. They don't have the same type of nerve system as humans. The filing doesn't offend them, it's the gigantic steel toothbrush they dislike.

Horses aren't crazy about having their teeth pulled either. Again, it isn't that it hurts. The horse just figures it's easier if he spits them out when he's ready.

The teeth a horse loses include his baby incisors and his baby molars. The baby incisors come out pretty easily, but often the baby molars hang around for a while. Frequently the baby molar will sit on top of the incoming permanent molar, and then it is known as a "cap."

A foal will get his first teeth — the two middle nippers — at the age of about two weeks. He should have all six of his incisors about the age of eight months.

When a horse gets his teeth, their size, shape, and markings can tell you his approximate age. This poem (1892) by Oscar Gleason will help determine the number of candles for the birthday cake:

TO TELL THE AGE OF A HORSE

To tell the age of any horse,
Inspect the lower jaw, of course
The sixth front tooth the tale will tell,
And every doubt and fear dispel.

Two middle "nippers" you behold
Before the colt is two weeks old.
Before eight weeks, two more will come;
Eight months, the "corners" cut the gum.

Two outside grooves will disappear
From middle two in just one year.
In two years from the second pair;
In three the corners, too, are bare.

At two, the middle "nippers" drop;
At three, the second pair can't stop.
When four years old, the third pair goes;
At five a full new set he shows.

The deep black spots will pass from view,
At six years, from the middle two.
The second pair at seven years;
At eight the spot each "corner" clears.

From middle "nippers," upper jaw,
At nine the black spots will withdraw.
The second pair at ten are white;
Eleven finds the "corners" light.

As time goes on, the horsemen know,
The oval teeth, three sided grow;
They longer get, project before,
Till twenty, which we know no more.

A mature horse has 40 teeth, while a mare has 36. The stallion or gelding has "tushes," or pointed teeth between the incisors and molars. Tushes are not always found in mares.

Sometimes horses and mares will develop small, pointed teeth in front of the molars of the upper jaw. These teeth are known as "wolf" teeth. They don't often appear in the lower jaw, but they can.

If a horse has all his teeth, plus wolf teeth, he could have as many as 44, while a mature mare could have as many as 40.

Most of the time it is a good idea to have wolf teeth removed, since they will frequently bother a horse while he is carrying a bit.

Horses don't often need an orthodontist. Usually they don't have crooked teeth. On occasion, however, they'll have teeth that don't meet properly. If the upper teeth stick out in front of the lower incisors, this is called, "parrot-mouthed."

When the lower teeth are in front of the uppers, then it is called an "undershot jaw."

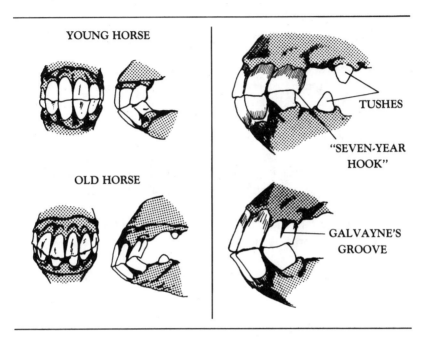

don't meet properly. If the upper teeth stick out in front of the lower incisors, this is called, "parrot-mouthed."

Both conditions are considered genetic defects, and horses with either condition should not be bred. Today, such conditions are not as serious as when virtually all horses grazed, having to bite off growing feed.

In the middle of all these teeth, a horse has a lot of tongue — 12 inches or more — the major function of which is the intake of food.

A horse's tongue, like ours, does have taste buds, but unlike ours, it is not used in the production of sounds.

Horses do bite their tongues on occasion, but most often injury to the tongue is caused by heavy-handed riders and/or use of severe bits.

Any serious cuts on a horse's tongue should be stitched. Small cuts or insignificant scratches in the mouth generally heal well on their own.

In addition to food intake and tasting, horses' tongues are good for "rolling the cricket of a bit," "licking salt blocks," and "sticking out" at people they both like and dislike.

Who Knows the Nose?

There isn't much information available about a horse's nose.

I don't think people who write books on horses like horses' noses. I don't think veterinarians know much about horses' noses.

Maybe that's being a little hard-nosed, but it's true.

Actually, the *Daily Racing Form* writes more about horses' noses than any other publication. Of course, the *Daily Racing Form* is often wrong when it reports a horse won "by a nose."

Horses actually win races by "an upper lip."

A horse's upper lip gets to the wire before his nose does. But it doesn't sound as good.

Horses' noses are also a little deceitful. You don't see all that's there. There aren't just two nostrils; there are actually four.

When a "drinker of the wind," is taking in air, he does so through the same nostrils he "flares." But he has other nostrils, inside the visible ones, which don't serve much of a purpose. In fact, I don't even know the purpose.

They're the false nostrils, and the only thing I know they do is vibrate. It's the vibrating of the false nostrils you hear when a horse is galloping hard.

Of course a horse uses his nose to smell. How important the sense of smell is to a horse is hard to tell.

We know a horse sniffs another horse when making his acquaintance. Or, at least we think one horse sniffs another. Mostly though, you'll find they blow more than sniff. And, they blow into each other's nostrils.

An old horseman once told me if I'd blow gently into a strange horse's nostril, the horse would like me, and not forget me.

I've been gently blowing into horses' nostrils ever since, but without any significant result.

As to the ability to detect odors, we are pretty sure the horse has a relatively keen sense. How much he relies on his ability to smell we are not sure, for he never just smells.

When a horse is investigating something, he uses his senses of sight and hearing in cooperation with his sense of smell. If you watch the horse closely, I suspect you'll never see him just look, or listen, or smell.

Of course, the most important function of a horse's nose is for breathing. A horse doesn't breath through his mouth. He always breathes through his nose.

Horses with great endurance or speed have nostrils capable of great expansion. Large nostrils facilitate large air intake.

When examining a horse, the observer should look carefully at the nostrils. At rest, the movement of the nasal openings should be even. There should be nothing spasmodic about their movement.

When the horse is stressed, the nostrils should expand. The expansion should also be even, rather than a sudden jerking open.

Horses are subject to nosebleeds. In most cases it is a condition known as "epistaxis," and it is not considered too serious. The membranes of the nose are very delicate and richly supplied with blood. A sudden increase in blood can cause a rupture. This sometimes happens with race horses. If it does, there is usually little loss of blood and almost immediate clotting.

Dusty, dry feed can cause a slight inflammation in the nostrils, which sometimes leads to a nosebleed.

The thing horses probably do best with their noses is stick them into other people's business.

No matter the breed, sex, or age of a horse, you'll find he more often than not has his nose somewhere it doesn't belong.

His nosey tendency goes back to his natural curiosity, and to the fact that if he's going to look or listen he's also got to smell.

For a horse, nose news is good news.

4

Does He Look Hungry?

He eats like a horse. (That isn't the same as he eats like a pig.) Horses eat a lot; they aren't sloppy.

Horses eat a lot, that is, if the owners feed them properly. Unfortunately, being underfed is the number one problem faced by most horses today.

It's not so much that the horseowner isn't trying to do right by his mount. It's more that the average horseowner doesn't know how, or how much, to feed.

Throwing a flake of hay over the corral fence twice a day just doesn't get it for a horse. First of all, a flake of hay probably isn't enough for a 1,000-pound horse. And secondly, a lot of the most nutritional part of the hay is lost before the horse gets to eat it.

It has been pretty well established by the best horse nutritionists that a horse doing light work needs at least 1.5 to 2 percent of his body weight daily in high-nutrition feed. A good, leafy, alfalfa hay will supply the nutritional (protein) value required. At 2 percent of body weight, that means a 1,000-pound horse should eat 20 pounds of hay daily just for maintenance.

If a 12-year-old girl is throwing the hay over the corral fence, you can be pretty sure she isn't throwing 10 pounds of hay each swing. She is probably throwing the first flake, regardless of weight, that falls off the bale.

To determine the value of hay, it should be tested, and to determine weight, the hay should be placed on a scale.

Needless to say, both measures are generally out of the question for the average horseowner.

So, there are rules of thumb that can be used to determine kind and amount of hay to be fed.

Rule 1. Buy leafy, thin-stemmed, good quality alfalfa or other high-quality hay from a reputable feed dealer. This will almost certainly assure the horse of getting a high-protein-content meal.

Rule 2. Feed enough hay so the horse leaves about a handful of stems still uneaten by the next mealtime. A horse that is cleaning up every little leaf and stick is probably underfed.

It is not necessary to feed the average horse grains. Light work means about three hours a day, and few of today's horses get anywhere near that amount of use.

Grains can be fed if the horse is thin and extra weight is desired, or they can be included as a portion of daily total feed if the horse appears in need of a higher energy level.

Most of the time the horse gets the 12 or 13 minerals he needs through his daily hay diet. However, salt may be lacking. Free feeding of salt, or, as an insurance policy, the free feeding of salt plus minerals, is recommended.

Vitamins and other supplements are not required unless a dietary deficiency has been diagnosed by a veterinarian.

"Easy keepers," they say, get fat on air. Don't believe it. Horses only get fat on feed.

If the horse is excessively fat, a change in total diet is called for.

Fat horses can be trimmed down by increasing their work and dropping their daily feed to 1.5 percent of body weight. Cut out all grain.

Knowing the amount to feed is only half the battle. How to feed is the other half.

Feed at least twice daily. Three times a day is better. The largest portion of the daily ration should be fed in the evening.

Allow the horse free access to water, or water before feeding.

The best feeder is a manger, on the ground.

Throwing feed onto the dirt usually results in the loss of hay leaf, the soiling of hay, and an increase in sand colic. It is also expensive.

Overhead feeders also contribute to a loss of the most nutritional part of the feed, the leaf, and are blamed in many cases for eye infections.

A manger on the ground is best for the horse for two reasons. Feed in a manger stays uncontaminated without significant loss, and it allows the horse to eat with his head down — his natural position. When his head is down, and he's eating a lot, he's eating like a horse.

Horses Seldom Burp

Horses seldom burp!

A real rogue, who has no social conscience and most likely has been gulping air along with his food, will, on occasion, burp.

But, for the most part, horses don't. It's not that they are so darned polite. It's that their digestive system is geared for one-way traffic only, and burping is therefore against their nature.

The equine digestive system plays a major role in the horse-mankind relationship. It was the digestive system that helped the horse become a work animal rather than a dinner.

Cattle were the first work animals, but their digestive system made it necessary for them to lie down and ruminate (chew their cud) during work hours. All these short breaks slowed progress, so man switched his attention to horses, which don't need "digestive time off."

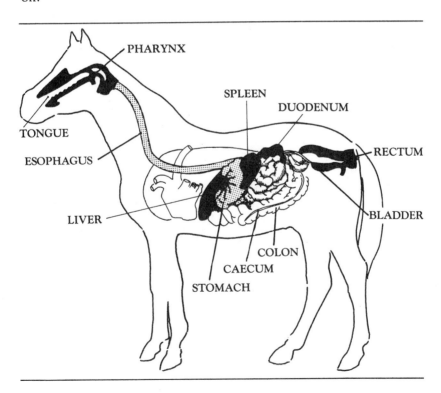

The horse's digestive system is made up of the alimentary canal — a muscular tube extending from the mouth to the anus — and the accessory organs, which are teeth, salivary glands, liver, and pancreas.

The mouth is the initial section of the alimentary canal. The horse is a polite, slow eater, and will spend quite a bit of time chewing his food. During the chewing, the food absorbs saliva, which aids in swallowing and triggers a chemical reaction that starts digestion of starches and sugars.

Food passed from the mouth to the next section, the pharynx, is trapped. It cannot return because at the rear of the mouth is the soft palate, a kind of curtain separating the mouth from the pharynx. The soft palate opens only on swallowing and, in effect, provides a one-way flow of food. (This is also the reason a horse can't breathe through his mouth, as can so many other animals.)

The pharynx sends the food on to the esophagus, which is 50 to 60 inches long and runs down the left side of the horse's neck to the stomach.

The muscles of the esophagus work in successive waves of constriction, sending the food into the stomach. Because the constriction waves of the esophagus muscles can work in only one direction, it is impossible for the horse to vomit. Anything that gets into the esophagus is going to the stomach.

The stomach is a muscular sac located in the abdominal cavity. The stomach is small in comparison to the size of the horse. This is attributable to the fact that the horse is a constant eater with no need for large capacity.

The stomach works in a compressive manner and also provides some digestive enzymes. But food begins passing out of the stomach as soon as the stomach is approximately two-thirds full.

The small intestine is about 70 feet long, and it continues the digestive process, adding enzymes from the pancreas and bile from the liver.

The large intestine is last. It is divided into four parts: the caecum, large colon, small colon, and rectum. The greater size of the large intestine allows the food to move along more slowly while the final digestion takes place.

A system of veins along the large intestine channel the greater portion of food-enriched blood to the liver, which is the major chemical conversion plant. The liver regulates the distribution of the nourishment.

While not too complicated, the digestive system of the horse does require some special care. That care is primarily seen in the horse-owner's feeding program.

The time of feeding, quality and amount of food, provision of adequate water, and manner of feeding are vitally important to the good health of the horse and normal functioning of his digestion.

If the feeding program is bad, it's tough on the horse.

There's no "plop, plop, fizz, fizz," for the horse's upset digestive system.

Pure Poison

Bargain hay or hay cubes are no bargain if they kill your horse.

As the price of hay increases, a recent University of California study shows, the number of horses being poisoned by contaminants in hay is also increasing.

And, as the price of hay goes up, often down goes the quality and amount being fed. A horse that is getting a low-quality hay, or not enough, often starts looking for anything to munch.

There are no fewer than 18 deadly plants horses frequently find to munch.

In hay, the two most common are fiddleneck and groundsel. Fiddleneck is a problem only during the first cutting of a new stand of alfalfa. Groundsel can be a first-cutting contaminant in the second year, or even in older stands.

On the West Coast, the common oleander plant accounts for a number of poisoned horses each year. One of the famous Budweiser Clydesdales died from oleander poisoning in a matter of hours. While being led past an oleander plant, the horse grabbed a mouthful of leaves. That was enough.

Castor beans are another common killer of horses. The castor bean is found most often in the southern regions of the U.S.

Chokecherries are found most often in woods, prairies, and orchards. They are large shrubs or trees and have pink and white flowers.

Bladder pod, or rattlebox, has flat pods and yellow flowers. It is most common in the eastern and central states.

Death camas grows in low grazing land and is frequently found in hay. It is an herb with a grass-like leaf.

Staggergrass, or staggerbush, is a spring and summer herb with a white, cone-shaped flower. Horses get at it when they are being given a treat and allowed to graze in natural pastures.

Horse nettle is a summer and fall plant that looks a lot like a tomato plant.

Jimson weed is usually found in well-worn pastures, and Johnson grass is found all year long, especially in the South. Johnson grass is a coarse grass with a white vein.

Ivybush is an eastern and northwestern shrub with a rose-colored flower.

Laurel cherry is found in the southern regions. It has a heavy cherry odor.

Milkweed grows all year long, especially along roadsides. It has a long silky pod and produces a milky sap.

There are a number of sorghum grasses found throughout the U.S. Sudan grass is a common name for one variety.

Yellow star thistle is found in the West, while yellow jasmine is found in the East. Both are deadly.

Water hemlock is a spring plant found in very wet open areas.

The best way to avoid these poisonous plants is by not letting your horse nibble while going on trail rides.

If you are putting your horse out to pasture, check with your State Department of Agriculture, which can provide helpful detailed information about poisonous plants. Then check the pasture carefully.

Don't buy bargain hay; buy from reputable dealers or feed stores.

When you do buy hay, always open a bale or two and check it for contaminants. If you find a lot of foreign matter in the hay, reject it.

And, upon the first signs your horse isn't feeling well — he may show colic signs, or stagger about, or get extremely nervous or tense — call a veterinarian.

There is seldom a cure, but immediate attention can sometimes save a horse from plant poisoning.

Cool, Clear Water

When pure, it is odorless, tasteless, transparent.

Without it, life on earth is impossible.

It is one of the best solvents. It makes up the greater proportion of the horse's body, and he likes to keep it that way.

It's chemical formula is H_2O. It's water, and more horses than not don't get enough, at least not enough of the right kind.

Without food, a horse could live about 50 days. Without water, he might live about 22 days.

Even the novice horseman gives careful consideration to the type and amount of food his horse gets, and there are plenty of vitamin and mineral supplements on the market to keep the average horse-owner busy guessing for years.

But who stops to make a careful appraisal of his horse's water supply? There are more horses in poor condition through lack of sufficient water than through lack of sufficient food.

There are three things to consider in providing the horse with water. How much he gets, when he gets it, and what kind he gets.

A 15- to 16-hand horse that is stabled, not doing hard work, and eating dry food, needs about 12 gallons of water each day during fairly cool weather. If the weather is hot and the horse is working hard, you can figure on doubling the amount.

A constant supply of fresh, clean water is best. The horse can then have water in the amount he wants whenever he's thirsty.

The horse's stomach has a lot to do with making this the preferred arrangement. The horse has a small stomach for his size, and the exit of the stomach is directly opposite the entrance and is larger than the entrance. So if you give water to a horse that has already started to eat, the fluid will wash undigested particles of food out of the stomach and into the intestines. This frequently results in colic, not to mention the fact that the digestive juices necessary for absorbtion of food will be diluted to such a degree that they may be rendered all-but ineffective.

Therefore, if the horse does not have free access to water, he should be watered before he is fed, never right after feeding.

It is also a poor idea to water a horse just before working him. The horse's stomach does not lie on the belly wall, but is suspended within the body of the horse. It lies against the diaphragm, which separates it from the lungs. If the stomach is filled with water or food, the capacity of the lungs to take in oxygen is reduced, and the horse will be under greater strain, which could lead to broken wind.

Contrary to popular belief, a horse may be given a drink while he is being worked, even if he is sweating. A horse that is hot from work can be allowed to drink, even cold water, providing the handler keeps the horse moving until he has cooled down. The mistake is not in letting the horse drink, but in giving him a drink and then not cooling him out properly.

Just like the rest of us, the horse needs clean, fresh water, not dirty, stagnant, or tainted water.

The automatic water device has many advantages. It gives the horse all the water he wants when he wants it. It saves time for the stable hands and it generally assures that the water used is clean and fresh.

However, automatic water devices must be checked to see that they haven't accidentally been plugged and that the bowl is kept scrupulously clean.

Large 30-gallon plastic trash barrels also make good water containers for horses. If checked twice a day, they provide a constant supply of water, and if they are cleaned regularly, the water stays fairly fresh. In addition, horses have a difficult time breaking them or getting themselves hurt.

Using the old-fashioned common watering trough is a bad practice, since it is usually not cleaned often enough and consequently provides an excellent means of spreading disease from one horse to another.

Every time you are thirsty and want something to drink, give a thought to your horse. He doesn't need a Cola or an un-Cola or a V-8. All he needs is a drink of fresh, clean water.

Lots of Chew, No Nutrition

When horses aren't kept as busy as little beavers, that's exactly what they become. And their wood sculpturing isn't highly appreciated.

Besides being detrimental to the appearance of wood fences and stall doors, wood chewing is a costly vice that can be quite dangerous to the horse. Splinters in the horse's stomach and intestines can cause colic; infection and internal bleeding and deaths linked to wood chewing are not unusual.

Wood chewing is generally a habit the horse develops out of nervousness or boredom. But it can also be a symptom of another serious problem. It can mean the horse lacks certain nutrients in his diet or his feed does not satisfy his natural desire for roughage.

What contributes to making our lives easier is not always good for the horse, and we often fail to recognize the needs of the horse.

Examples of human thoughtlessness that can lead to wood chewing include feeding the horse pellets instead of roughage, using small box stalls, and not giving the horse sufficient exercise.

From the owner's viewpoint, pellets are a convenient form of feed. But studies by Dr. G.F.W. Haenlein indicate that horses fed pellets develop a strong urge to chew after their appetites have been satisfied. The only experiment I ever conducted with pellets proved to me that Dr. Haenlein's more extensive research was absolutely correct.

Keeping horses in box stalls certainly makes their care a lot easier and, for some owners, stalls or small pens may be the only solution to lack of space. But the 12×12-foot structure doesn't make a lot of sense for the horse.

Being confined in a small place can have negative psychological effects on the horse. He cannot see all the activity, normally quite interesting to the average horse. He cannot run and play at will, and he cannot graze over great distances. Wood chewing becomes a way in which the stalled horse demonstrates his displeasure with his cozy cottage.

Nervousness caused by lack of exercise often results in wood chewing. The horse simply has excess energy that he can't get rid of. Eventually, he finds that wood chewing relieves some of the tension, just as many humans get rid of their nervous frustration by biting their nails.

If wood chewing indicates the horse is missing a nutrient, it is usually salt. Be sure the horse has free access to a salt block, or is fed about a handful of table salt each day.

If lack of roughage is causing wood chewing, a return to hay may solve the problem, unless the vice has become a habit. According to Dr. Tony J. Cunha of California Polytechnic University at Pomona, a horse's minimum hay requirement per day is .5 percent of his body weight, or five pounds of hay per 1,000 pounds of body weight. Dr. Cunha says hay also provides necessary bulk and fiber to prevent digestive troubles.

Horses that are fed hay, or a hay and concentrate diet, usually spend more time eating; consequently they have less time for wood chewing.

Reducing nervous tension, eliminating boredom, and supplying the proper roughage and nutrients are the only satisfactory solutions to the wood chewing problem.

Solutions that are dangerous, costly, or ineffective after a short period of time include the use of Tabasco sauce or other hot spices, covering stall doors or fence rails with woven wire or metal strips, or the use of electrified wire above the area to be protected.

Everybody Likes a Treat

Every year we celebrate holidays with special meals. Why shouldn't our horses?

They should, and can!

Treats for horses are good for horses, nutritionally and psychologically. (Note of caution: just like treats for humans, treats for horses shouldn't be overdone. Too much of a good thing can result in a tummyache.)

We like to start our holiday meals with an appetizer. So do horses.

Before the main course of hay, let's tickle his palate with some sliced carrots, a big sticky gob of honey or molasses, some sugar cubes, or even sliced fruit.

If not fed in overly large amounts, all are good for the horse, and will certainly stimulate his desire to eat. In fact, these appetizers are good for poor eaters anytime.

If you think you get tired of Hamburger Helper, just think how tired of hay a horse gets. A little appetizer a half hour before mealtime can really perk him up.

Of course, you should try to discover why the horse is a poor eater and correct the problem. It may just be a monotonous diet, but it could also be nerves, stress, poor health, or a lack of exercise.

Now for that special meal.

Roots bring toots of happiness as a first course.

Carrots are the basic root. Add some parsnips, rutabagas, turnips, potatoes, or sugar beets in small amounts and you've got a really delicious beginning.

When preparing the roots, be sure they are cut finely enough to keep the horse from choking.

If you're not inclined to go with the roots as a first course, how about a special relish?

Pumpkins, squash, and melons, sliced and in small amounts, are excellent. And don't worry about the seeds. When fed in small amounts, the seeds are not harmful to horses. Such fruits contain only 6 to 10 percent dry matter, so the nutritive value is low in comparison with cereal grains. Therefore, the horse still needs plenty of hay as the main course.

Entree: hay.

If your horse doesn't normally get grain, then he'll surely enjoy a pound or so with his hay to make the meal sumptuous.

And if you want to add a tantalizing sauce, pour on some molasses or honey. If you just want to jazz up the normal meal a little, sprinkle the hay with sugar.

Dessert is always special to a horse, if it is a compote.

Desserts, as always, are small. An apple a day is a good guiding rule. But, on special occasions, throw in a plum, a pear, a peach, or a nectarine. Be sure the pit has been removed from stone fruits prior to serving.

And, when the special holiday meal is done, and everyone is retiring to their favorite chairs, rubbing their tummies and saying, "I ate too much," don't forget Dobbin.

You want an after-dinner mint, and so does he.

According to my daughter, Cathy, Polos, English candy mints, are the best. But, they are hard to get in the U.S. She says peppermint Life Savers are almost as good.

One mint is enough for me.

Most of our horses, however, are not satisfied with fewer than three.

5

What's Normal?

When I was feeling a little sick, or ran a little temperature, or had a touch of the well-known "Pip," my mom would put me to bed and give me a little chicken soup.

Chicken soup, of course, cured everything!

But, there's no such miracle cure for horses.

Rest, good food, and fresh water, plus a tincture of time constitute the basic cure for horse ailments — for horses, it's the closest thing to chicken soup. When the problem requires greater medical skill, call the veterinarian.

How do you know when to call the hoss doctor? By reading the horse's vital signs: temperature, respiration, and pulse.

As you get to know your horse well, you'll recognize immediately when he isn't feeling up to par. That's the time to get out the thermometer.

The normal temperature for a horse is 99° to 100°. A temperature of 101° is common in young foals.

A horse with a temperature of 105° or 106° is usually a very sick horse.

To check the horse's temperature, shake the thermometer to get the mercury down, then lubricate the thermometer and insert it full length into the horse's rectum. Before inserting, it is a very good idea to attach a length of string to the top of the thermometer. Hang on to the string and the thermometer won't be lost.

The thermometer should be left in for at least three minutes.

The respiration rate is the number of times a horse inhales and exhales each minute. The average rate for the complete cycle for a horse at rest is 16. But that is an average and may not be normal for your horse. You'll have to check the respiration over a three- or four-day period to discover the normal, at rest, rate for your horse. This will give you something to measure against right away when you think he isn't well.

The best way to determine respiration is to place your hand on the side of the rib cage and count the number of breaths taken as you time with the second hand of your watch for one minute. Another way is to stand back from the horse and watch the in and out motion of the rib cage, or the opening and closing of the nostrils, and count in the same manner.

If the horse has just been worked, or is excited, the respiration rate can climb to 30 or 40 and still be normal. The rate you want to know is the "at rest" rate.

The pulse rate, at rest, is normally just a little more than double the respiration rate. So a horse with a 16 respiration would have about a 36 pulse. Like the respiration rate, the pulse will increase with stress or exercise.

The pulse is the throb or surge of force in the artery as the heart pumps blood through the body.

The easiest location to find the pulse is usually the artery that runs along the inner side of the horse's jaw.

Other convenient locations are at the back of the fetlock joint and the inside of the elbow.

It's a good idea to practice taking your horse's vital signs. The practice will not only help you to read the signs more easily, it will establish what is "normal" for your horse.

Take the vital signs at different times of the day and over a three- or four-day period. Be sure to write down the results each time. You'll find the signs are slightly different under different circumstances, but always fall into a three- or four-point range, If there is a 10-point variance from normal, the "alert" sign is flashing.

The next time your horse "doesn't look right" you can take his vitals. If he's in his normal range, maybe all he needs is a little of the "chicken soup doctoring."

But if he's not normal, he'll need a veterinarian, and the veterinarian will be happy to know you've already started the diagnosis procedure.

What Condition Is Your Horse's Condition In?

When you really want to know what condition your horse's condition is in, you've got to do a little more than "eyeball" it.

The horse's general state of health is a good indicator of the horse's general condition, but it doesn't tell the whole story.

Most experienced horsemen know when a horse is feeling good. They know when a horse is on the muscle. They know when the horse is ready to put forth his maximum effort.

The problem is the condition of the horse's condition may not be at its maximum. The horse's maximum effort for his current condition may not be his peak potential. He may lose the race by a nose. He may fatigue after 48 miles of a 50-mile endurance test. He may come up sore and sour after a weekend ride in the hills.

You can look at a horse and see he's in good condition. But you've got to check inside to determine if he's at his peak of condition.

Many of the measurements related to condition involve the circulatory system, which is made up of the heart (pump) and the vessels for carrying blood throughout the body. An analysis of blood, the fluid that carries oxygen, nourishes all cells, removes waste, and fights disease, can give a good indication of the horse's stamina, or performance capability.

Measurements of the red blood cells are most frequently considered when attempting to determine state of condition of the equine athlete. Red blood cells carry oxygen, and without an adequate supply of oxygen to meet the requirements of working muscles, the horse simply will not have the stamina or strength to win.

One of the most valuable analyses is hematocrit value, commonly known as packed cell volume (PVC). PVC is a percentage count of the red blood cells.

There are many, many factors that can influence the PVC, however, and 35 percent is considered average. A top performance horse in condition will probably be closer to 48 percent.

The red blood cell count should normally measure between 9 and 12 million cells per cubic millimeter for light horses and from 7 to 10 million for draft horses. A blood count lower than the guide is termed anemia. Anemia has many causes, but the first consideration might be given to nutritional deficiencies.

Serious disease, such as heart disease or emphysema, can cause the red blood cell count to be higher than average.

Measurements of hemoglobin are indicators of the oxygen-carrying capacity of the blood and are considered an index to performance potential. The hemoglobin concentration is measured in grams per 100 milliliters of blood. Most horses have a normal concentration of between 13 and 15 grams per 100 milliliters of blood. Some research indicates that hemoglobin concentration and total blood volume can be used to predict racing performance and physical "readiness" of the horse to work.

White blood cell count is not ordinarily used to predict a horse's performance potential, but it can do so by calling attention to an adverse condition.

The normal white blood cell count is between 8,000 and 11,000 cells per cubic millimeter. If the count is higher, it usually indicates some type of bacterial infection, and consequently a reduced performance.

Blood tests should be taken by a veterinarian and the analysis done by a reputable laboratory. For them to be beneficial, the horseman needs several tests to determine what is "normal" for a particular horse. Once normal is established, improvements or problems can be charted.

Whether hot-blooded, cold-blooded, or blue blood, the best condition is knowing the condition of the condition.

Ouch!

Every time you turn around a horse has another cut, scrape, bump, lump, slash, or puncture.

Sometimes they need a little loving care, sometimes they need some professional medical treatment, and always they need a little attention.

The first rule of first aid for horses is to treat all injuries as soon as they are discovered. The initial treatment may be very minor, such as rinsing off the injury with clear water. In any case, you must make your first treatment in such a manner as to be of assistance to further treatment and proper healing.

Don't take action too quickly. Putting the wrong medication on a wound may cause severe complications.

Don't take any action too slowly. Some injuries need emergency first aid and professional treatment within hours.

Using the proper time frame is probably the best way to determine whether or not you have an injury that simply needs care, needs emergency first aid, or needs professional medical attention.

If you have a bleeding wound, the question is one of survival. A horse can lose a lot of blood, but not for long. A slow dripping or running of blood, which lasts less than 10 minutes, is not too serious.

A heavy flow of blood lasting longer than 10 minutes is very serious; it is an emergency.

Wounds without a lot of bleeding can still be considered emergencies if they are deep, and they need suturing within one to two hours. Leg wounds fall into this category.

Wounds on the face can wait for four to six hours for suturing, and body wounds should be sutured within three hours.

All other wounds, scrapes, lumps, and bumps are probably not emergency injuries, though you may want to have a professional look at them and you should give them plenty of "loving care."

Major blows to the body, which may not show much more on the surface, can often be "need professional attention" candidates. A horse that falls, or runs into a fence, or kicks a solid object, then shows some signs of lameness or an inability to move normally, should be seen by your veterinarian.

Horses that scrape the hide off a spot or two, or have a shallow cut that is not too long, generally need only "loving care."

If the injury falls into the "needs first aid" category, you must take two actions: call the veterinarian and apply the initial treatment while waiting for assistance.

In applying the initial treatment you must do a combination of three or four things.

1. Get the horse to a safe place and free the injured area of contamination as best you can. This usually means running cold, clear water from a hose onto the wound. If running water is unavailable, get a bucket or pan of water and sponge the wound. If you can't do that, don't mess with it.
2. Run cool, clear water onto the wound to keep it clean, and to keep the swelling down.
3. If the wound is bleeding, you may apply a compress. A compress should be bulky and can be made of clean towels.
4. Determine the status of the horse's tetanus immunization; your veterinarian will want to know.

It is a very wise horseman who keeps the rules of first aid treatment in mind.

In case all else slips your mind, you may want to try a final rule I use.

If I faint, everyone calls everyone!

Oh, My Tummy Aches!

Colic is a killer, yet it isn't a disease.

It's a stomachache — horse size!

Colic is the name we give to any undiagnosed abdominal pain the horse suffers. In many cases, the horse is treated for colic and the specific cause of the trouble is never identified.

But we could significantly reduce the number of stomachaches if we wormed our horses regularly. According to a report by the American Association of Equine Practitioners, almost "ninety percent of all colic cases result from damage done by bloodworms."

In order to prevent the other 10 percent, we'll have to look for other colic causes.

Colic can be caused by a sudden change in feed. Horses should be introduced to new feeds gradually, especially lush, green feeds.

Moldy feed can cause colic, as can an irregular and sporadic feeding schedule. Establish both the amount you feed and the time you feed your horse and then stick to the schedule.

Just as with people, colic can be caused by overeating, or the overeating can cause gas, which results in colic. And it doesn't matter how you spell relief, the product isn't available to the horse.

To make matters worse for the horse, unlike a lot of human over-eaters, the horse has a very difficult time burping, and he can't vomit.

Other contributors to colic are cribbing, too much water after a hard workout, and poor teeth, which keep the horse from chewing his food properly.

A common cause of colic is sand impaction, which means the horse has ingested sand with his food. Do not put your horse's feed on the ground, and be sure the horse is getting enough to eat so he isn't sifting through the soil looking for a stem of hay.

No matter the cause, the signs of colic include restlessness and sweating. A colicky horse will often pace or paw the ground, and frequently he will break out in a mild or sometimes heavy sweat.

If you ask your horse what's bothering him, he'll often look at his sides, or he'll bite at his sides or rub his sides against the wall or fence. If your horse is in severe pain, he may even kick at his sides.

Certainly the horse with colic will not eat and most likely will not drink. He may moan a good deal, and if you put your ear to his side, you'll not hear a lot of stomach noise. Under normal conditions, you'll hear the workings of the stomach and intestines. But when a horse is suffering from colic, normal internal work is shut down.

Finally, the colicky horse will frequently throw himself about in agony. He may get down and roll, which many believe can result in a twisted intestine. Actually horses roll all the time and don't twist an intestine, so this fear is probably without basis.

If your horse shows any of these signs, act immediately. Call your veterinarian.

Make the call even though some cases of colic may disappear on their own; it's always better to be safe than sorry.

The veterinarian may ask the horse's temperature, what you have been feeding, how long the horse has had the symptoms, when he was last treated for worms, and what recent activity the horse has had. Be sure you are ready with the answers.

You should then follow any advice the vet gives.

While you are waiting for a veterinarian, it is best if you walk or jog the horse. This may help relieve a gas pocket, which may be the cause of the colic. Don't overexert the horse, however. The idea is to relax him, not make him tired.

When a horse has a tummyache, act quickly and get professional help, because colic can kill.

An Interesting Contradiction

There are all kinds of conceptual contradictions in the horse world, and inflammation is one of them.

Inflammation can be both good and bad at the same time.

And to relieve the bad effects of inflammation, horsemen often create more — deliberately — in the hope that what exists will be healed in a shorter length of time.

Inflammation is a reaction of the body to injury, and is commonly characterized by heat, redness, swelling, pain, and disturbed function.

Since inflammation is a natural response of animal tissue to injury, inflammation is present every time the horse sprains, strains, bumps, twists, cuts, or punctures some part of his body. It also occurs when the horse is attacked internally by viruses, bacteria, chemicals, or parasites.

The immediate reaction to an injury is usually swelling of the surface of the injured area of the horse's body; redness is also noted.

The body sends an increased supply of blood to the injured area, much as we would send extra fire fighting units to a major blaze. Because the white blood cells are responsible for removing contamination and debris caused by the injury, a larger than normal supply is needed at the scene.

The purpose, then, of natural inflammation is to kill infectious agents, prevent the spread of disease, clean up the damage caused by the injury, and heal the injured area.

But sometimes horsemen want to hasten the natural healing process.

This is done in two ways. The first is to clean the injury and make it as free of contamination as possible. This creates the most advantageous climate for the body to heal itself.

Also, a horseman may create additional inflammation intentionally by using an agent that actually causes more damage to the affected area, thus dilating even more blood vessels to assure an even greater supply of blood.

An example is "blistering" a horse if the animal has shin bucked. When a horse shin bucks, the tissue along the front of the cannon bone is damaged and natural inflammation is immediate. The application of a blister (through use of a caustic agent) encourages additional swelling due to the increased blood supply, and it creates additional discomfort for the horse. The only good part about induced inflammation is that the injury often heals more quickly.

The horseman could also treat the injury by letting the horse rest, thus preventing additional damage to the tissue, and by cooling the damaged area. This is accomplished by running cold water onto the cannon bones, reducing the swelling by deterring the increase of blood, and thereby lessening the pain associated with the swelling and heat.

Given enough time, the natural healing process usually repairs or replaces the damaged tissues and restores good health to the area.

Ordinarily, when horsemen talk of inflammation, they don't use the term itself; they indicate what is inflamed by adding "itis" to the word for the affected area of the horse. For example, an inflamed tendon is called "tendonitis," whereas an inflammation on the horse's skin would be dermatitis.

When a horse is injured, inflammation is beneficial because it is part of the natural healing process. At the same time, inflammation is bad because it creates swelling, congestion, pain, and heat.

And inflammation is even more contradictory because horsemen often make it worse in order to make it better.

New Name, Old Problem

It may be time to change the name "Monday Morning Disease (azoturia)" to "Show Horse Syndrome."

For one thing the name azoturia has been proved incorrect. The name originates from azote, the French word for nitrogen, indicating an abnormal amount of nitrogen in the urine. That usually is not the case.

The name "Monday Morning Disease" was applied years ago because so many work horses suffered the affliction when they went back to work following a weekend of rest.

Today, the syndrome strikes on any day of the week, and it is seen most frequently in mares normally getting a consistent amount of healthy exercise and plenty of feed — show horses.

Azoturia is characterized by reddish brown or almost black urine, muscle stiffness, especially of the hindquarters and loin, on occasion by profuse sweating, and by obvious signs of pain.

Sometimes fatal, azoturia hits suddenly. The horse appears perfectly normal, maybe even a little on the "high" side when taken from the stall. Very shortly after exercise begins, the visual signs appear. The horse's breathing may be hurried, and the muscle stiffness is evident. In severe cases, total lameness in the hindquarters will probably occur, and the horse could go down.

The horse, of course, will not want to be moved, and should not be.

Get the horse into a stall and let it rest, or leave it where it is if the stall or corral is a good distance away.

What has occurred when a horse is stricken is that glycogen, a kind of blood sugar stored in the muscle tissue, has started to break down. A by-product of glycogen breakdown is lactic acid. A buildup of lactic acid in the muscle tissue results in a partial spasm or "tie-up."

Most veterinarians treat the azoturia symptom cases by first giving the horse a tranquilizer, which helps relax the muscles, and an injection of vitamin E and selenium. The horse is then rested for a day, after which it begins a very light exercise program.

Of course the horse's diet is changed so the animal is not getting grain for a day or two. When grain is again given, it is given in small amounts and increased gradually.

Bandages Should Protect

A woman called me over and asked, "Would you check this bandage and see if it is all right?"

"Why are you bandaging the horse?" I aksed.

"Because she's sore, and I want to work her."

I didn't ask why she wanted to work the mare when the mare was sore. I looked at the bandage. It was a shipping boot applied over cotton.

"This is not an exercise bandage," I said. I removed the bandage from the left leg, and my gosh, what a surprise, the mare was beginning to bow.

"There's a lot of heat here," I said.

I took the bandage off the right leg. Same condition. I suggested she call her veterinarian before working the mare. "There could be a little problem here," I said.

I've found that bandages, like bell boots and splint boots, are often used for no specific reason other than they look "professional."

A professional bandage doesn't have a "look" unless it's one of neatness. A professional bandage is not there to be seen. It's there to prevent, protect, or help a healing process.

It is not necessary that a bandage always be started in a certain place, or that it end in a certain place. What is necessary is that the bandage stays on and does the job it was intended to do.

The biggest danger with bandages is that they are misapplied — so tight they cut off circulation or not flexible enough to give with the movement of the horse.

Bandages put on by the novice horseman are often quite neat, and just as often serve no function.

The shipping bandage is the most common. The handler usually wraps the bandage neatly (and, of course, it matches the color of the horse's blanket, and the trailer, and gate post to the side paddock), but fails to cover the area most frequently injured: the pastern and coronet.

Shipping boots are okay, if they are pulled down over the pastern and coronet, but I personally like a bandage.

The best materials for wrapping the leg are heavy cotton sheets and heavy flannel strips. The strips should be about six inches wide. A good knit bandage can also be used.

There is no need to wrap in a certain way, but the preferred method is to always wrap from the inside out. Start by placing the cotton on the inside of the leg in the groove between the tendon and cannon bone. Then bring the cotton forward and across the cannon, then around the leg. Do the same with the flannel strips.

Many old-time horsemen suggest the finished bandage be fastened with safety pins. While this has been done for years at the race tracks, I'm a thoroughly modern Millie. Most knit bandages have tie-strings or Velcro fasteners.

If you use the flannel strips, a roll of inexpensive one-half-inch masking tape works wonders. A couple of turns with the tape and you have a safe, secure bandage.

If the horse is being bandaged with braces or sweats, the same bandaging materials are normally used. (It is often common practice, however, to put the sweat on, then cover with a plastic wrap. The plastic is followed by the cotton, then the flannel strips.)

When medications are being applied, it is the wise horseman who checks first with his veterinarian concerning the medication, the need for additional protection, and the length of time the bandage should be left in place.

I like to remove a bandage both morning and night just to make sure circulation is good and that the leg remains clean and is progressing as expected.

An exercise bandage should have some elastic properties so it can be pulled tightly enough not to slip. If cotton is used under the exercise wrap, then it must be thin cotton. If the padding under an exercise wrap is too heavy, it can lump and cause excessive pressure in specific areas. Bowed tendons are frequently caused by misapplied exercise bandages.

There are special bandages for special problems, such as the spider bandage, which can be used to protect an injured hock or knee. Such bandages have very specialized uses, so consult a vet before applying them.

Before applying a bandage, ask yourself: Will it protect, prevent, or help in the healing process? If it hasn't got a specific purpose, it doesn't look good, it looks "out of place."

The Same, But Different

There is very little difference between strangles and dry land distemper. Yet there are a lot of differences!

Strangles, which is distemper, is a bacterial infection caused by *Streptococcus equi*. Dry land distemper is an infection caused by *Corynebacterim pseudotuberculosis*, reports Dr. Byrd.

Stangles is common throughout the U.S., while dry land distemper seems to be confined to the West.

Strangles causes pronounced swelling in the lymph nodes and glands in the area of the throat, which often cuts off the horse's air supply — hence the name "strangles." Dry land distemper also affects the lymph nodes of the throat, but frequently attacks the muscle groups in the chest and along the ventral midline (belly).

Strangles was once often a fatal disease, but today, with adequate treatment, it is not considered to be a major threat. Dry land distemper is usually a rather mild, if unpleasant, disease.

The horse with strangles will generally show signs of a stiff neck, a high fever, nasal discharge, a cough, a lack of appetite. The horse with dry land distemper will exhibit painful, hot swellings and occasional lameness, but doesn't usually show much of a temperature.

Strangles is a highly contagious disease and is spread by purulent material from ruptured lymph nodes. It can be injested by a healthy horse or inhaled as droplets. Common water troughs, feed buckets, blankets, and brushes can be sources of infection.

Dry land distemper is infectious, but not highly contagious. It is spread by flies that bite both diseased and healthy horses along the ventral midline.

The similarities and the differences are easily recognizable, but positive proof that a horse has one or the other of the diseases can only be determined in a laboratory. Material from an abscess must be analyzed, says Dr. Byrd.

It is important a veterinarian be consulted when a horse shows signs of either disease, since the proper action early will usually prevent any serious complications or permanent aftereffects.

The great problem with either disease is the possibility of internal infections, which can be extremely dangerous.

If strangles or dry land distemper is suspected, the horseowner should request an examination by a veterinarian. While waiting for the vet's visit, the horse should be treated as if the problem is strangles.

Isolate the horse immediately. And don't give antibiotics without first consulting your veterinarian. In many cases antibiotics will only slow down the process and complicate matters.

Your veterinarian may not prescribe medications, but may advise hot packs and/or external poultices to speed up the abscess process.

There are no preventive actions against dry land distemper, but there is a vaccine against strangles. However, the vaccine can have some ill effects and should be given only on the advice of your veterinarian.

If you have horses, sooner or later you are going to see one or both diseases. Strangles is most common in very young horses, but, just like dry land distemper, can attack a horse of any age.

Now that you know the differences, you know your first action should be to treat them the same.

The Medicine Chest

If you're like me, your medicine cabinet is full of a lot of things that can't be used, and only a few things that can.

It's the same with your horse's medicine chest. It's probably loaded with a lot of things that are no longer worth having. What is needed is hard, if not impossible, to find.

The trick is to clean it out periodically. Then restock it.

And don't overdo it! You really don't need as much as your horseochondriac thinks.

You'll need a thermometer. Get a good one. Thermometers are all hard to read. You can roll them in your fingers a hundred times and still not see the mercury. So, select a thermometer on the basis of how easy it is to read.

You'll need some blunt surgical scissors. It's not so much that you might need to protect your horse when you have to cut a difficult bandage from him; the blunt points are so you won't stick yourself when he moves.

You'll need several rolls of cotton. These are for leg injuries; don't let them out of their wraps for any other purpose. Once a roll of cotton sees daylight it will immediately fall into the dirt, tear itself, and absorb shavings into its layers.

Rolls of cotton should be forbidden to move.

A small bag of cotton balls. (A small bag will last a thousand years since you won't use the cotton balls often. They are primarily there to keep you from touching the rolls of cotton.)

Several rolls of gauze, store at least eight quilted pads to use with leg wraps, and four cotton knit leg wraps with any type of fastener except string ties.

A bottle of rubbing alcohol is required, as is your favorite nonirritating antiseptic topical dressing. You should also have a bottle of your favorite liniment. Horse liniments are used on sore and swollen muscles or on the legs to create circulation and give relief to stretched or pulled tendons or ligaments.

I like a liniment that has a pleasant aroma, since I also like to have it rubbed into my sore back muscles.

It is a good idea to have a supply of clean rags, towels, and soap. Dish soap in a plastic squeeze bottle is pretty good. The soap and towels can be used to wash your hands prior to and after treating a wound, and the rags can be used to scrub up a scratch or abrasion.

You'll need some adhesive tape for putting on a bandage that needs pressure. A roll of masking tape is excellent for holding the end of a leg wrap when applying a standing bandage.

A little Vaseline or mineral oil is good as a lubricating agent. Either will work as a hoof dressing.

You'll need a cheap bottle of bleach for treatment of thrush.

I like to have a supply of Butazolidin tablets. I keep them and my bottle of aspirin handy. This way both the horse and I can get some quick minor pain relief.

I have a rule: Never give shots unless specifically directed by the veterinarian. I think it is a bad policy for the horseowner to administer medications. If a treatment requires follow-up — say the veterinarian wants you to give 20 cc of whatever each day for the next four days — well, then you do it. Otherwise, don't give shots; so don't keep needles or syringes.

Do keep a notebook and pencil handy. They're good for jotting down remedies, telephone numbers, shopping lists, and the dates various medications were given your horse.

Invariably the veterinarian asks, "When was the last time Diablo had . . .?"

You'll put the veterinarian into shock if you check the notebook and reply, "You administered it on June 1, about 9:30 A.M. You were late, again, that day."

[Additional copies of the following Equine Health Record appear on pages 113-116.]

EQUINE HEALTH RECORD

NAME _____ IDENT _____ COLOR _____

BIRTH DATE _____ SEX _____ OWNER _____

CHRONIC PROBLEMS _____

DRUG ALLERGIES _____

VACCINATION RECORD

Tetanus Toxoid	Encephalomyelitis				

WORMING RECORD

Date	Method	Drug	Date	Method	Drug	Date	Method	Drug

LABORATORY TESTS

Date	Test	Results

RECOMMENDED HEALTH PROCEDURES

Worming:

Horses One Year or Older — Treatment for all worms twice a year (Dec.-June). Treatment for bloodworms (Strongyles) orally in feed every 8 weeks.

Foals — First worming at 2-3 months. Repeat at 3 month intervals.

Broodmares — Twice a year, generally Nov.-Dec. and midsummer. Do not worm after 9 months of pregnancy except for specially selected treatment.

Vaccination:

Tetanus Antitoxin — Duration of protection not more than 10 days. To be given following injury to an animal that has not received tetanus toxoid.

Tetanus Toxoid — Duration of protection at least 1 year. Two injections 30-60 days apart. Booster given yearly.

Encephalomyelitis (Sleeping Sickness) — Duration of protection for season of infection. Two injections 7-14 days apart during May-July. (This and tetanus toxoid vaccination to start at about 4 months of age.

Teeth:

Saddle & Breeding Animals — Check yearly. Float if necessary.

Racing Animals — Check and float twice a year.

Foaling Mares:

Mare — Tetanus antitoxin or toxoid.

Foal — Tetanus antitoxin or toxoid and penn strep-enema if needed.

BREEDING RECORD

Estrus Date		Date Bred	Pregnancy Exam.		Comments
In Date	Out Date		Date	Diagnosis	

DIAGNOSIS AND TREATMENT RECORD

Date	Diagnosis	Treatment and Remarks

MISCELLANEOUS INFORMATION

Date	Remarks

SHOEING AND TRIMMING RECORD   *T-Trim   S-Shoe

*	Date	*	Date	*	Date	*	Date	*	Date	*	Date	*	Date

Special Shoeing Requirements: _____

6

Up His Nose with a Rubber Hose

While the chances of ridding your horse of worms are somewhere between slim and none, the chances of your horse dying from worm-related problems range from good to very good.

According to Dr. John B. Herrick of Iowa State University, more than "fifty percent of all horses die directly or indirectly from internal parasites."

And according to a report sponsored by the American Association of Equine Practitioners (AAEP) and the Morris Animal Foundation, nearly "ninety percent of all colic cases result from damage done by bloodworms (*Strongylus vulgaris*)."

You really don't need to know what to look for to determine whether or not your horse has worms — I can assure you he does. However, the most noticeable external signs are rough hair, a pot belly, fever, coughs, listlessness, diarrhea, dull or watery eyes, and poor growth. Any of these signs, alone or in combination, indicate the worm problem could be severe.

But even if your horse has a shiny coat, is fat, and appears to be quite healthy, the horse probably is infested with worms.

T. J. Fogg, D.V.M., conducted an extensive study in the field of equine parasitology, and the resulting data are terrifying.

A total of 429 horses from all parts of the country were used. The survey found 98.5 percent were infected with small strongyle. Bot fly larvae infected 95.1 percent, and *Strongylus vulgaris*, perhaps the most devastating parasite, was present in 83 percent of the horses.

Bloodworm was found in 79 percent, while a second species of bot fly was discovered in 66 percent of the horses.

Dr. Fogg found geographic location did have a notable affect in the parasite populations. The small strongyles occurred in 98 percent of the horses in both East and West, but in the East the *Strongylus edentatus* was most common. In the West, *Strongylus vulgaris* was the most common. The West also had a much higher occurrence of the second type of bot fly; 75 percent infection as compared to 46.1 percent infection in the East.

The study confirmed the older the horse the greater the likelihood of parasites. Surprisingly, however, the study indicated horses one to six months of age had a lot of parasites, including bots, which aren't supposed to infect young animals.

Strongylus vulgaris gets its name, bloodworm, because as an adult, it sucks blood after it attaches itself firmly to the walls of the large intestine. It is while the bloodworm is attached to the walls of the intestine that the female deposits large numbers of eggs, which pass with horse droppings to the ground.

Once on the ground, the worm larvae hatch, then fasten themselves to grass, which the horse eats. Back inside the horse, the larvae migrate for about six months before returning and maturing in the intestines to reestablish the cycle.

The large bloodworm attaches itself to the intestine wall, sucks blood, can block blood flow, and damages artery walls.

Small bloodworms burrow into the intestinal lining, causing ulcers and interfering with the horse's digestion.

Bots, a fly larvae, damage a horse's tongue, lips, and throat, as well as interfering with digestion once they have attached themselves to the stomach wall.

Roundworm larvae will migrate through the horse's body, penetrating the intestinal wall, the liver, and the lungs. Especially dangerous to young horses, roundworms can grow to be a foot in length and can block the intestine or puncture it.

Pinworms in large numbers can upset digestion and sometimes cause anemia. Pinworms are quite often the cause of "tail itch."

Owners should give special attention to new foals, as roundworms will severely retard the absorbtion of needed nutrients, stunting the foal's growth. They may even block the foal's intestines, resulting in death. This can, and has, happened to foals as young as three months.

Worms are a problem all year long and are virtually impossible to eliminate because of the structure of their life cycle.

Having a horse wormed, by tube or otherwise, kills most of the adult and immature worms. However, there are still thousands of eggs remaining in the horse and ready to hatch at different times. In addition to the eggs, the migrating larvae, which move through the horse's body for six months or longer, most likely will not be affected by the medication. The larvae become adult worms, laying more eggs, while the other eggs are being passed out of the horse, then reswallowed to become new larvae.

To make the battle even rougher, a single horse with an average worm infection, may be depositing up to 25 million new eggs per day in his manure. The results are obvious.

If everything you have read so far is scary, give some thought to this fact: The majority of horseowners don't know as much about worms as you have just read.

But don't panic. You can do a lot to minimize the parasite problem.

Because the life cycle of the worm is continuous, any worming program must also be continuous. Get the advice of your veterinarian and begin a regular health program immediately. Don't miss a single horse, no matter how healthy he appears.

Many vets recommend tube worming twice a year — usually around the first of June and the first of December. In addition, they usually recommend a feed additive wormer about every eight weeks.

There are a number of good feed additive wormers available at the local feed or tack store, or from your vet. Keep records and administer the medications on schedule.

If your horse is finicky and won't eat the medication in his grain, try adding a little molasses — just enough to disguise the taste and hold the medication in the grain.

Or try raspberry-flavored Jello. Many horses love raspberries.

For several days prior to worming, mix the dry Jello with your horse's feed. On the third or fourth day, add the wormer to the Jello and grain and watch him become a happier, healthier horse.

Tetanus and Other "Shots"

I got bitten by a horse.

He was a nice horse until he bit me. Then he was a mean, nasty, bad stallion, and I told him so.

The bite broke the skin; the wound bled and then turned a nice deep purple.

Did I need a tetanus shot?

Every horseman should know the answer, but few do. I didn't , so

I decided to ask members of my equestrian college class of more than 30 men and women.

"You need a tetanus shot every year," one said.

"No, you don't," said another. "You'll be all right. Don't worry about it."

A young woman said, "If it broke the skin, you'll have to take the painful Pasteur treatment." She was obviously referring to the infamous Pasteur remedy for rabies, a malady I might have feared had I been bitten by a dog.

It was clear what had to be done. Call the veterinarian, then call my doctor.

Both the veterinarian and the medical doctor agreed. Immunization against tetanus is very important, especially for horses and horsemen. Tetanus bacteria hate oxygen, like dirt, and are thrilled about horse manure.

Tetanus is always around horses, says Dr. Byrd, and it is a killer, so it's a good idea to have your horses immunized.

"Although tetanus is present with all wounds, it is much more common if the wound was made by a puncture," Dr. Byrd says. "Tetanus bacteria like to get away from oxygen, and do very well in a deep, contaminated puncture."

To protect your horse, you should start a toxoid program. This involves two injections of tetanus toxoid four to six weeks apart, and then booster shots at one-year intervals. It is wise to keep a record showing your horse's toxoid program is up to date.

There is a lot of confusion among horsemen about tetanus toxoid and tetanus antitoxin, according to Dr. Byrd. One is safe, the other much less so.

Tetanus toxoid is quite safe, effective, and long-lasting. The only adverse effect ever observed is an occasional and temporary swelling at the point of injection.

On the other hand, tetanus antitoxin often gives excellent protection for two to three weeks, but its use sometimes results in serious and possibly fatal aftereffects, Dr. Byrd says. The problem with antitoxin is that it contains horse serum, and horse serum injections are too frequently followed by equine serum hepatitis, which can be fatal, warns Dr. Byrd.

Why may a veterinarian be forced to use tetanus antitoxin in spite of its drawbacks? In the absence of records or knowledge that the horse is being protected by a current toxoid program, he must use the antitoxin because it gives immediate protection, whereas toxoid does not, unless the horse is on such a protective program.

Because of the risks of using antitoxin, it is wise to start your horse on a toxoid program and keep him on one.

The main symptom of tetanus is muscle stiffening. The animal has a rigid posture with the head and tail extended. Usually the first muscles affected are those of the jaws, thus the name, lockjaw.

In humans, the incubation period of tetanus is 2 to 50 days, says Peter G. Van Etten, M.D. The most frequent symptom is, of course, a stiffness of muscles, especially in the jaws.

Dr. Van Etten assured me I wouldn't get tetanus from the bite, while pointing out that the tetanus spore might be on my skin and thereby get into the wound.

"Tetanus is dangerous and there are still a number of deaths from tetanus," he says, "chiefly among the young and old."

Most people should probably be immunized about every 10 years, but a person working with horses should be immunized every 5 years. If you suffer a wound, it should be washed immediately, and then treated, he adds.

The tetanus shot doesn't hurt when you first get the needle. It hurts the next day.

I got the shot in my arm because it's hard to sit on a horse when you've had the shot in your bottom.

Your horse should also have vaccinations for encephalomyelitis (sleeping sickness), rhinopneumonitis, and influenza.

Equine influenza is a very contagious disease caused by two of the viruses in the influenza A group (termed equine influenza A-1 and A-2). Influenza attacks the respiratory tract and is associated with "cold symptoms."

Rhinopneumonitis is a mild disease of the upper respiratory tract caused by a specific virus that can also cause abortions.

Encephalomyelitis is also caused by a virus, and we principally vaccinate against two: eastern and western. There is a third virus, Venezuelan, but we haven't had a problem with it since 1971.

Be sure to consult your veterinarian concerning the recommended vaccinations for your area, and be sure to keep a record so you know when your horse had his primary, secondary, and booster immunizations.

Horses Need Exercise

Exercise is defined as "active use to give practice and training or to cause improvement."

It can also be described as "getting out and moving about; kicking up your heels."

Most horses don't get enough exercise.

How do we know that?

We know because studies indicate too many of our horses are too fat, and too many have nasty stall vices, and too many have too many injuries that are associated with poor physical condition.

If they are getting too little, how much is enough?

I often ask this question, but I seldom get a very satisfactory answer.

We know horses in the wild will move an average of 30 miles per day just looking for food, water, and a good place to snooze. But, what we don't really know is what constitutes enough exercise for a domesticated horse.

One renowned expert devotes a whole paragraph to exercise in his complete encyclopedia on horses. He says, horses should exercise as much as possible on pasture. If no pasture is available, exercise mature animals for an hour or two a day under saddle or in harness.

Thanks much, but that just doesn't get it.

Obviously different amounts of exercise are correct for different horses. Young horses don't need the same type of exercise as an older jumper.

A medical expert advises a horse's daily exercise should consist of enough work to make the horse's pulse, respiration, and perspiration output increase to the point where at least one of the three is noticeable.

That's not good enough either. If we follow that guide, all we know for sure is that exertion has taken place.

I think we have to go back to the definition of exercise: "active use to give practice and training or to cause improvement."

A young horse in a round pen or on a longe line is going to show improvement in gait, pace, stopping ability, or just in paying attention, about the same time he's had enough exercise to rid himself of all his excess energies. It won't be coincidental that his pulse and respiration are elevated or that he's just started to break a sweat on his neck.

An older horse in training is going to need a few minutes just to warm up. So the rule of "walk the first mile out" might be a good guide for starters. Then we can go to work on the performance lessons, past and present.

Using the definition of exercise, we'll know the horse has had enough about the time he starts to show "improvement in his work."

Just to make sure he's had enough exercise we can "walk him the last mile back."

There's another type of exercise every horse needs. Every horse should have some time alone, free to roam. Turn him out in a paddock or a pasture, or even a training ring. Be sure he's got enough room to run, stop, turn, kick up his heels, and get the kinks out.

Once a week, or once a month, you'll find the free exercise period will "improve" a horse's mind.

If you aren't going to turn him out, or longe him, or ride him, then at least get him walked every day.

Hand-walking a horse isn't all that much fun, so hot walkers are dandy. A young horse should have at least a half hour on a hot walker if he is to get no other exercise that day. A mature horse that is being worked four or five days a week will need at least an hour on a hot walker.

The amount of work a horse received used to be measured in hours. A light work was from one to three hours; a heavy work from four to eight hours.

But time alone doesn't measure the true relationship between exercise and the horse's present physical condition.

Active use to give practice to an individual horse's skills or to cause improvement of those skills is a darn good guide to how much exercise is the right amount for that horse.

And if your riding skills aren't improving every day, *you* need a little more exercise!

It Feels Good — To Him!

Grooming a horse is hard work!

To do the grooming job properly, you'll need a mane and tail comb, a metal curry comb, a rubber brush, a stiff brush, a soft brush, and a hoof pick.

For proper grooming — the kind that brings blue ribbons — you'll also need, although not necessarily for daily use, a pair of small electric clippers and a pair of large electric clippers, shampoo, a water scraper, soft rags, and a bottle of baby oil. You should also have a hood, blanket, and tail wrap.

Wow! It takes a lot of equipment.

Daily grooming is given just prior to working the horse. This grooming consists of removing mud and long hair with the metal curry comb, a quick rub with the rubber brush, a brief rub with the stiff brush (sometimes called a rice straw brush), and a once-over-lightly with the soft brush.

Use the mane and tail comb to remove tangles. Do the forelock as well as the mane and tail.

Do not use anything but the soft brush or a clean cloth on the horse's face.

Do not use the metal curry or the rubber brush below the knees and hocks.

Make sure you brush behind the fetlock joint and on the outside of the ears.

Always clean the horse's feet with the hoof pick before and after asking the horse for work.

The metal curry is used in a scraping manner, going in the direction of the hair.

The rubber brush is used by rubbing it in small circles, and the soft and stiff brushes always brush in the direction of the hair.

During the brushing phase of grooming, look for cuts, scrapes, or nicks on the horse. If you find any, apply an antiseptic dressing. Also check carefully for any hock sores or nicks around the coronet band and dress them.

Make it an unbreakable rule never to put your horse away dirty. I don't recommend frequent baths with soap or shampoos, as soap takes the natural oils from his coat. But, I do suggest you give him a cool, clear water bath daily if the weather permits.

If you have not rinsed or bathed your horse after you have worked him, then you'll need to use lots of elbow grease and take plenty of time for the second phase of your daily grooming program.

Start with the rubber brush and give your horse a good rubdown. He likes it and it's good exercise for you. It also brings the dirt to the surface and removes most of the loose hairs.

A careful brushing with the stiff brush follows. Make sure you brush the horse thoroughly, including the hard-to-reach spots between the front legs, inside the back legs and under the chin.

A complete going-over with the soft brush comes next. Be sure to do the face and ears with this brush.

I prefer taking care of the mane and tail a little at a time rather than having to do the job all at once. This seems an easier way for both you and the horse. Let's start with the mane.

Never use scissors. Always "pull" the mane, tail, and forelock in this manner: Take hold of a small section of the mane. Hold onto the long hairs to be "pulled" and backcomb the remaining hairs out of the way. Wrap the long hairs you are holding around the comb and pull out with a sharp jerk. Repeat until you have removed the long hairs from the entire mane.

The length of the mane is generally determined by the breed and by what is most acceptable in your part of the country.

When you "pull" a horse's tail, begin with the top of the tail and jerk the short underneath hairs out. Short hairs sticking out make the tail look unkempt. You can keep a tail wrap on a horse that has an exceptionally bad tail or on one that rubs his tail.

The tail is considered short when it reaches only to the horse's hocks. But remember, when a horse is standing still, the tail should reach a little below the hocks because the horse will hold his tail out from his body while he is moving, making the tail look even shorter than it really is.

To get the tail to the desired length, simply tie a knot in the tail where you want it to end. Then pull out those hairs that hang below the knot.

The forelock is left heavy on certain breeds and in some parts of the country. Personally, I prefer a thin forelock that is not too long.

You can thin and shorten the forelock the same as you do the mane.

It is a good idea to keep your horse blanketed.

A heavy blanket worn in winter will keep the horse's hair smooth, and a day sheet worn in summer keeps the hairs from being bleached by the sun. If you do blanket your horse, always remember to give him a few hours in the sun each day without the blanket, as horses absorb vitamins from the sun through their skin. If you live in a severely cold climate, you may want to add a hood and neck wrap to keep the neck and face hairs smooth.

About a week before showing a horse, get out the electric clippers.

Using the large clippers, start with the front legs, left side. Face the rear of the horse. Pick up the leg, holding it in your left hand. The palm of your hand should be on the cannon bone just above the fetlock joint. The foot will then hang down a little bit, permitting you to clip the back of the pastern and the back of the coronet band easily. Run the clippers against the hair from the coronet band to the fetlock joint. Do not clip against the hair above the fetlock joint except around the ergot.

When the back of the pastern is done, move the leg out in front of the horse and turn around so you now face in the same direction as the horse. Rest his leg on your right knee and clip the pastern from the coronet band to the fetlock joint.

Now set the foot down and clip from the knee down to the fetlock joint by running the clippers with the hair down the cannon bone. Clip behind the knee in the same way.

The rear legs are clipped in the same manner as the front legs.

However, you will find it harder to get to the back of the pastern on the rear legs. Sometimes it is easier to clip the back of the pastern if the horse is standing with his rear feet squarely under him.

Before clipping the bridle path with the large clippers, decide how long you want it to be. A fairly long bridle path helps make a horse appear to have a narrow throat and a longer neck. A short bridle path does just the opposite and should be used if you want the horse's neck to look heavier.

Start clipping the bridle path at the farthest point down the neck and clip up the neck to the poll. Make the first cut on an angle as this makes the mane lie over and look better. Be careful you do not cut into the forelock.

Use the large clippers under the horse's chin and to remove the long hairs at the throatlatch.

The small clippers are used around the muzzle, in the ears, and to remove the long hairs that grow just under and above the eyes. You will find that most horses do not like having the hair in their ears clipped. It is best to start by trying to clip the ears without using any form of restraint on the animal. If the horse will not cooperate, then go to a lip chain or a twitch.

Do not tie your horse while you are clipping him. Have someone hold him or simply leave him ground tied.

If weather permits, you may give your horse a bath a day or two before the show.

Before you shampoo, give the horse a thorough rubdown with the rubber brush. Wet your horse all over before applying the shampoo and be careful you do not get shampoo in his ears, eyes, or nostrils. Shampoo the entire horse.

You do not want to leave any soap on the horse's skin so make sure you rinse him thoroughly. Use clear, lukewarm water and do the job carefully and completely. Make sure you wash and rinse the horse well between and behind the back legs.

The mane and tail can be washed with horse or human shampoo or you may prefer to use a special mane and tail shampoo. There are also special soaps with bleach to make your horse's white markings brighter.

After you have rinsed the horse thoroughly, use the water scraper to remove the excess water. Pay particular attention to the area under his belly as this is where the water collects.

Take your horse to a shaded area to let him dry. If he stands in the sun to dry, the sun makes the ends of the hair curl.

When he is dry, use the stiff brush as your first grooming tool, following it with the soft brush. Brush the horse thoroughly with both brushes. Now use a soft cloth dampened with baby oil or a prepared coat dressing. Some prepared dressings come in spray cans, but you must rub these dressings in if you want them to do a really good job. Rub the cloth with the baby oil or coat dressing all over the horse, including his mane, tail, and forelock.

When you have finished this task, blanket your horse and keep him blanketed until show time. The blanket keeps the hair in place and helps the coat retain the natural oils. If your horse has white socks, it's a good idea to wrap his legs.

When show day arrives, you'll go through the entire grooming program again.

Just before you enter the show ring, you'll want to apply baby oil around the horse's eyes. This makes the eyes look larger and brighter. Also put baby oil around the muzzle as this brings out the color and gives the head much more appeal.

Rub your horse down lightly with a soft rag between classes. The rag, treated with a little baby oil, picks up the dust from his coat and has him shining for the next class.

7

A Place to Hang a Halter

A horse's house is his home.

And he really gets attached to it.

While there are a lot of slobs around who will live in a sloppy house, a horse won't — if he's got a choice.

Horses are basically pretty neat and tidy.

When they've got a neatness problem, it's often circumstances. Horses will make a wet spot in a small corral or box stall because they urinate in the same place. The horse's idea of using the same spot all the time is a good one. The builder's idea of not using an absorbent base material is a bad one.

Pipe corrals that measure 12 by 12 feet or 12 by 24 feet are becoming very popular — with horseowners, not necessarily with horses. From a horse's point of view they are too small, hard to keep clean, often don't give protection from the sun and rain, and frequently are dangerously constructed.

If a horse is to live in a small corral, then plan on providing the horse with plenty of exercise. Plan to keep the corral raked clean, daily. Wet spots need repair, daily.

A pipe corral should have some type of roofing, at least over half of it. Horses should not be left to bake in the summer sun or stand in the rain for days on end.

It's not the rain that's so bad, it's the mud.

Pipe corrals get terribly muddy and mucky. It's virtually impossible to keep them dry. But the area under the roofing can be built up — before it rains.

Once the rains start, the area under the roofing can be improved by the additions of sand or shavings.

Water buckets or automatic waterers should be placed so they are shaded at least part of the day, yet are not directly adjacent to the manger. Water and waste hay draw flies; but even worse, in combination they produce mold and become toxic.

Many pipe corrals are poorly constructed. They have nuts and bolts and sharp edges in all the places that horses like to stick their ears, noses, and eyes. The consequences can be tragic, and the veterinarian's bills can be a lot higher than the initial investment in a good pipe corral.

A good pasture makes a great house for a horse.

But it's got to be a good pasture. Many aren't.

A good pasture has shelter; maybe natural, maybe man-made. A big tree is terrific.

A good pasture has plenty of fresh water, doesn't flood badly, has some high spots, is free of dangerous obstacles and noxious weeds. A good pasture is well fenced.

It is not necessary for a good pasture to provide the horse with food. The owner of the horse should know the nutritional value of the pasture, and take appropriate action.

Barns and box stalls can be palaces or dungeons.

Good box stalls are in good repair. That means the walls haven't been chewed in half and left that way. That means there aren't nails and eyebolts sticking out of every wall. That means the door closes without falling off the hinges.

To be a palace, a box stall must have good light and good ventilation. It should be cool in the summer, warm in the winter, and dry when it rains.

If a horse sweats or freezes or can't see another horse, then his barn or box stall is "solitary confinement."

And if a box stall or barn isn't cleaned and rebedded daily, if the flooring isn't freshened weekly, if the construction isn't safe, the horse that lives in that house isn't going to be happy.

Deep down inside, every horse likes a neat, clean, tidy, fresh castle. It makes him feel good when friends come to visit.

Fight the Good Fight

The horse fly problem seems to be worse than ever, every year.

Nothing you can do will be completely effective, but there are some steps you can take to make life a little more bearable for your horse and a lot less pleasant for the flies.

First, eliminate fly breeding areas, such as piles of damp hay and manure and muddy areas around water containers.

Use a wipe type fly repellant consistently in the morning and afternoon. I've found that fly sprays blow away before you get them on the horse. They are not economical, and they seldom work. The wipe doesn't work either unless you change brands every two weeks, but they seem to do some good for short periods of time.

Be careful, however. If you put too much repellent on a horse, it will cause tiny sores and the horse may develop patch losses of hair, especially around the face.

You can try brewer's yeast. Feed two tablespoons to each horse every two or three days. After about 30 days, your horse should not be bothered by flies. But brewer's yeast doesn't always work.

So you can try apple cider vinegar. Give each horse a half a cup of apple cider vinegar each day. Your horse should not be bothered by flies after about two weeks. But vinegar also doesn't always work.

Another suggestion. If you have a stall, close the doors and shade the windows and hang a eucalyptus branch inside. This method seems to work best if the horse gets a lot of work before he is closed in the stall. Otherwise, he eats the branch and tears down the window shades and lets in all the flies.

You can't win! But you can fight the good fight, and a fly swatter helps!

Hot Days Are Hard

Hot, hot, hot, hot!

Long, hot summer days are just as hard on horses as they are on you. Maybe harder.

Summer requires some preparation if the horse is going to survive. And since the horse can't pick up a hammock, a sunshade, and a lemonade at the local hardware store, it's up to you.

A little additional thought and an extra few minutes of time will do the trick.

With the first heat wave, the horse's daily diet should undergo a change, just as yours does. You eat a lot more salads, cold cuts, and easy-to-fix dinners. The horse, however, just wants less hot foods. Cut out the "hot" grains, and substitute some extra hay, or pellets, or hay cubes.

With the heat you don't dress the same. Bikinis don't suit horses, but a reduction in weight does. Get the horse's weight down and he'll feel a lot better during the summer.

We perspire when it's hot, and the horse sweats. In both cases, there is a salt loss. The horse needs more salt during the summer months, and it's easy to give him plenty. (More about salt in the next section.)

Finally, make sure your horse is prepared for summer by being sure the water supply is adequate and functional.

Some horses will drink 30 gallons or more of water a day during the summer. The water bucket must be large enough and filled often enough to quench that kind of thirst.

If you use automatic waterers, great! But be sure they are working, and are not in the direct sun. With the "push" type, the lever can become so hot a horse won't touch it with his nose. Or, if the water pipes are in the direct sun, the water can get so hot the horse can't drink it.

Summer riding, of course, is a lot of fun when both parties can enjoy it.

Ride in the early morning or the evening, when it is cool. Don't ride during the hottest part of the day. And keep in mind that you may be able to take the sun, but you aren't doing all the work. (If you don't want to pick up a 25-pound sack of grain and run around the yard with it, the horse probably doesn't want to haul you around either.)

Warm the horse up before you start a ride. That may sound silly on a hot day, but it should be done. A warm-up period for the horse accelerates his breathing, which raises the oxygen level in the blood. The horse needs a good oxygen level to work well, especially in the heat.

When riding in the heat your horse will sweat. Sweating is his way of expelling heat. However, if the horse gets too hot he'll stop sweating or his breathing will become very rapid. (The rapid breathing is an attempt to fill his lungs with cooler air to reduce his body temperature. A horse cannot pant like a dog to help expel heat.)

A horse that is overheated should be walked out until cool and given small amounts of cool water periodically. Don't let the horse drink as much cold water as he wants. If the horse appears dehydrated, or so tired he won't walk, call a veterinarian immediately.

If the horse has had a good ride, and is just sweating, walk him until the sweat dries, then give him a nice cool, clear water bath and walk him until he dries. Put him away with a friendly pat.

There will be days so hot you won't want to do any riding. Neither will the horse. On those days make yourself and your horse as comfortable as possible.

But, on many summer days you and the horse will be hot to trot.

More About Salt

As you sit around the pool sipping iced tea and catching a few rays to improve that summer tan, think about your horse and say, "salt."

The salt block you put in the manger last summer and the salt contained in the prepared grain mix you feed may not be sufficient.

As the temperature and humidity climb, you perspire and your horse sweats. It's the body's way of reducing heat buildup. The more the sweat loss, the greater the need for salt and trace mineral replacement.

The average horse needs 50 to 60 grams of salt per day. On a warm day, a horse may easily lose that much salt through sweating and urination. If he is worked moderately, he will lose even more.

To replace that amount of lost salt, the horse will have to have about a four-ounce intake of salt, according to the U.S. National Research Council. (You'll have to make your own determination about your horse's salt need by observing his behavior and condition.)

Salt and trace minerals play a very important role in keeping the horse healthy. And a big loss of salt through sweating can lead to a change in the horse's behavior and condition.

A horse deficient in salt and trace minerals usually shows it through physical and behavioral reactions.

Chewing on fences or mangers and eating dirt are behavioral changes.

Physical reactions can be noted in weight losses, rough coat, and listless eyes. In addition, the horse may exhibit fatigue when worked.

Significant loss of electrolytes (salts dissolved in body fluids) can also lead to excessive fatigue, muscle spasms and cramps, dehydration and exhaustion. These conditions are normally seen during stress situations, but can also result from moderate work during very hot weather.

The amount of salt contained in hay and grain may be fine during the winter, but may not be sufficient during the summer.

Since most prepared grain mixes list salt and trace minerals as ingredients, but don't tell you how much, you can't rely on them to provide enough salt.

So it's to the horse's benefit if you have salt constantly available in loose-salt form. Loose salt is easier for the horse to eat than block salt. Unlike cattle, the horse has a smooth tongue, so he cannot easily get enough salt by licking a block.

When a horse is in desperate need of salt, he will sometimes chew off big hunks from a salt block, or consume the whole thing. This can cause a colic condition.

Iodized salt, or the red blocks, are not usually as well liked by horses as the white block.

Do not salt a horse once a week, a practice that is fairly common, but incorrect. A horse cannot store salt in his system, so he'll be oversupplied one day, short the next.

Salt serves the horse in a number of ways. It stimulates the secretion of saliva, making food more palatable and aiding in digestion.

As a nutrient, it provides sodium and chlorine, which are necessary to establish and maintain the correct electrolytic balance.

A horse that is getting enough salt each day will enjoy better health and will have greater endurance.

When Winter Winds Blow

Tramping through the mud in a cold, cutting rain isn't any fun, for man or horse. But, it's a fact of life when winter winds blow.

In a man's case, it's pretty easy to get out of the rain. But for too many horses, it's impossible.

Luckily, horses are pretty hardy creatures and take care of themselves quite well, even in a snowstorm. But when they are "protected" by man, the problems of neglect occur. (It's often all too easy to say, "He'll be all right," as you sit in front of the fire and listen to the constant cold rain.)

If kept in a small pen, or pasture, a lot of horses aren't going to be all right, unless they get a little help from their friends.

Without some attention, thousands of horses will suffer mud fever, cracked heels, rain scald, or thrush this winter.

Mud fever is a condition that results from the horse standing in constant dampness for prolonged periods, such as being fetlock deep in mud for a week or two. It can even occur when a horse stands in a stall of damp shavings.

The moisture on the lower legs weakens the skin, which is irritated by the mud and dirt. Eventually the skin cracks and is attacked by bacterial or fungal infections. Mud fever can even occur on the upper legs and belly if the horse must lie down in the mud.

Cracked heels is a similar problem normally seen at the groove at the back of the foot between the bulbs of the heels. Infections here exude serum and pus commonly called, "grease."

Rain scald is most often seen on the rump and back. Similar to mud fever, it too is an infection caused by constant dampness and then chapping of the skin.

Thrush attacks the frog and sole of the foot, and is again associated with constant dampness, plus mud or dirt.

All of these conditions can be extremely painful, can result in lameness, and are preventable with a little effort on the part of the horseowner.

It is not a good idea to shave the hair from the legs of any horse that will be standing in a small, exposed corral or pasture. The hair on the legs is a good protection and should be left.

If the horse is going to be "out in the elements" this winter, some type of overhead protection is needed. The shelter need not be elaborate or fancy, but it must provide the horse the opportunity to remain fairly dry for periods of time.

Dry footing is a must. The horse can run around in the mud most of the time, but he needs a spot of high ground so his legs and feet can dry out now and then. The area need not be big, it simply needs to be dry.

A wind break — hedges, trees, canvas, wood fencing — is just fine as long as it gives the horse an opportunity to get away from a scalding, chapping wind.

Waterproof blankets are a big help for horses if someone checks the blanket for dampness periodically. The horse is better off without any blanket than with a wet blanket.

To protect the legs from mud fever and cracked heels, the horse's legs should be washed clean, then dried, and finally coated with Vaseline, lard, or, better still, a zinc and caster oil ointment. Any of these applications should be cleaned off every few days and reapplied.

The hoofs can be protected to a great degree by the application of a hoof dressing. Those containing lanolin are especially effective.

Finally, the horse that is going to be "out" needs a good balanced diet with an oily supplement, such as linseed meal or cod liver oil.

These minor efforts can help the horse avoid any or all of the painful conditions he's subjected to by the nasty days of winter and thoughtless owners. But, even with an ounce of prevention, total protection is not assured.

If any of these winter ailments should appear, the horse should be housed in a dry, clean stall immediately.

The affected areas should be cleansed with lukewarm water and a mild antiseptic, then kept dry. It's a good idea to have the horse checked by a veterinarian.

Winter can be miserable, and it's unavoidable. Cracked heels, mud fever, rain scald, and thrush are also miserable, but they are avoidable.

Just Snoozing

Once you get your horse's housing needs taken care of and have prepared him for all seasons, what do you suppose he's going to spend his time doing?

Well, horses spend the second greatest portion of their lives resting. (Feeding occupies the greatest portion, as if you didn't know.)

Horses rest in three distinct ways. They doze, they slumber, and they deep sleep.

When dozing, horses all take on the same basic posture and expression: the neck horizontal and relaxed; the lower lip droops a little; a greater percentage of their weight is on the forehand; and they bend one hock and rest the toe of the hoof.

Horses can doze anywhere and at any time. The horse doesn't fully rest when dozing. Although his front legs have a nifty anatomical structure that allows him to rest while standing better than other animals, the muscles of his hind legs are not at full rest.

You will notice that every few minutes the horse will shift his weight and rest the opposite hind foot.

When dozing, horses seem to be totally unaware of what is going on; but they are not. A dozing horse can move very, very quickly, can kick with accuracy, and can bolt. Few will ever catch a dozing horse unaware and off guard.

Since adult horses can rest quite well while standing, they lie down only when they feel completely safe. Many horses foaled and raised on small farms or ranches will lie down more frequently than horses that have moved from place to place or were raised on a big ranch. Backyard horses generally have little to fear and usually don't have well-developed herd instincts.

When a horse slumbers, he'll lie with both his front and hind feet under his body, and he'll usually bend his neck toward his feet, then rest his chin on the ground. If in a herd, slumbering horses will always have a standing horse on guard duty. The guard horse is not a special horse, just the one that didn't get down soon enough. The guard horse will remain on duty until one of the slumbering horses rises.

Even with horses raised in small pastures, the rule of guard duty applies. Surprisingly enough, it also remains true with horses in box stalls. You can check 20 box stalls at any time, day or night, and you'll never find all the horses slumbering. At least one stands guard duty.

In deep sleep the horse lies on its side, usually with one front leg bent and both back legs stretched.

If you are very observant about horses' sleeping patterns, there is no need for a pregnancy test on mares, according to some authorities. Once pregnant, mares will not lie completely over on their sides in deep sleep, I have been told.

Most horses awake quite quickly from any type of sleep. Once up from slumber or a deep sleep, they will stretch and yawn, loosen their muscles, and go about the day's business, which consists mostly of dozing.

8

Everyone Grows Older

Who's happy about January 1 being the official birthday for most registered horses?

Certainly not the new foal. Not the mare. Not the stallion. Not the owners or the exhibitors.

Then who?

The bookkeepers, that's who!

To make it convenient for record keepers, January 1 was established as the official birthday for horses by most breed registries, regardless of when the horse was foaled. And that means a young horse, whether six days, six weeks, or six months old, becomes one year old on the January 1 following his birth. Thereafter, he leaps into a new age bracket with the passing of each calendar year.

Foals and mares don't like the January 1 birthday. It's a cold, wet, windy, snowy, silly time to give birth.

It's not nice to fool Mother Nature, who knows it's best for horses to be born in the late spring, when the temperatures are warmer and the grass is greener.

Mother Nature shows her displeasure at man's attempts to force artificial early breeding seasons by giving the horse a low conception rate (the average being less than 50 percent) and a high mortality rate among newborns. The conception rate exceeds 70 percent only at the very best breeding establishments.

According to studies by Dr. O. J. Ginther at the University of Wisconsin, the best time for breeding mares is May 12 to October 10, which means the foal would appear approximately 11 months, 10 days later, or anywhere from April to September.

And studies done by Colorado State University have established the best breeding time for stallions is in June. Semen output is highest during the latter part of the established breeding season, and is double in July what it is in January.

But with January 1 being the official birthday, show and race horse owners refuse to think of waiting to breed mares in July and August. They believe it is to their advantage to have a foal born as close as possible to January 1. They believe an early foal should be bigger, stronger, better-muscled, and faster than one born later in the year, even though they are — on the record book — the same age.

And show judges seem to think the same way. They usually pick the largest and most mature-looking horse in a class. In fact, it's the subject of much conversation when a judge picks a young horse over older stallions or mares in a grand champion class.

But Mother Nature may be fooling us all.

The records show that even though we are attempting to force an early birthday so we'll have more winners, it isn't working.

A study by the American Quarter Horse Association of winners of the All American Futurity, the world's richest race, during a 10-year period, reveals one winner was foaled in January, two in February, three in March, one in April, two in May, and one in June. The average birth date was March 27.

Two more random studies showed the average birth date of 73 American Quarter Horse Association champions to be March 28. And the average birth date of 829 Register of Merit winners was April 8.

March 1 would be a better official birthday. Let the bookkeepers enter that in their records.

There Will Be More

It's breeding season again.

All the magazines have just published their Stallion Editions, and all the advertisements are pleading with you to bring your mare to Hot Stuff or Super Duper or The Winner.

Well, I'm pleading with you not to breed your mare, unless:

1. You know what you want.

Don't breed a mare just to get a foal, just because you think it would be nice. In the long and short run, breeding on that basis is a disaster.

The net results will include a financial loss for you, and probably a pretty miserable life for the foal. Foals bred on this basis too often end up being a burden to the breeder, never being put to a useful life, and for the most part neglected.

Breed for a pleasure horse, or halter horse, or race horse, or a horse to sell. But know what it is you want.

And once you know what it is you want, study the market. Map out a plan to get you what you want. Don't take chances.

Like begets like. It's not very often that two slow horses are going to produce one fast horse. Or that two poorly conformed horses are going to produce a top halter prospect.

Only dummies breed without knowing what they're trying to get.

2. Don't breed your mare unless she's really worth breeding.

The difference between horsemen and dudes is obvious when you hear a person say, "Well, if she can't run, we'll breed her."

Horsemen don't breed mares that have proved they aren't good at what it is they are supposed to do.

If a mare can't run, she isn't a super prospect to produce good running horses. Now there are plenty of mares that were unraced and produced stakes winners, but you can bet they had the blood.

If a mare has poor conformation, don't expect her to give you a halter winner. If she's predisposed to lameness, expect her foals to inherit her weaknesses.

Probably the worst mistake you can make in the breeding business is to take a mare who can't perform and try to produce performers.

She'll cost you a fortune, because like begets like.

3. Don't breed your mare unless you can afford to breed to the best stallions.

There are too many bad stallions around. My guess is that 70 percent of them would make nice geldings, and there'd still be too many bad stallions.

If a mare shouldn't be bred because she didn't measure up to a high standard, then a stallion shouldn't be bred unless he measures up. Be sure he does. No excuses!

Picking a stallion based on the breeding fee is a poor genetic selection.

So, please, don't breed your mare unless you know what you want, and she's worth breeding, and you can book to a good stallion.

Like begets like.

If You're Going to Breed, Study Genetics

What everyone wants is a champion. What everyone gets is an opportunity to pay their money and take their chance.

Genetics, or the science of heredity, is supposed to be important to the horse breeder because, through its study, we should be able to produce a horse with the predictable inheritable traits we want.

So let's make a quick study of genetics.

Horses have 64 chromosomes arranged in 32 pairs. Each chromosome carries many thousands of genes. These genes contain all the information about what the new horse will be.

Now if the genes would behave themselves, we might make a pretty accurate prediction about the new foal's inheritable traits, such as how fast he could run, his size, disposition, color, etc.

But genes are ornery little devils and they have what we call "variable expressivity." A simple example of variable expressivity is that all chestnut horses are not the same shade of chestnut. In other words, some of the genes expressed themselves a little differently.

Genes give the new foal two types of inheritance. The first is qualitative and the second is quantitative.

There are relatively few qualitative genes and lots of quantitative genes; those which are quantitative are affected by the new foal's environment.

There is a medium to high degree of inheritability in the speed of a horse, but the speed trait comes from quantitative genes and is therefore influenced by life-style, food, sunshine, training techniques, etc.

So to select the right stallion for our mare, hoping to get a very fast foal, we need to know about the quantitative genes and environments of both parents.

The stallion may have average quantitative speed genes that got a whole lot of help from his environment. Or he may have had a lot of speed from genes that weren't helped at all by his environment.

This information is difficult to acquire, but we can do several things in order to find good breeding stock.

1. Compare the records of stallions' performances. Don't worry about the pedigree of a horse further back than three generations, as the great-grandsire will have little influence on your foal.
2. Select from the very best lines. You can ignore 90 percent of the available stallions, as they should have been gelded long ago.
3. Try to find a superior breeding animal, one with prepotency (homozygously dominant genes). How do you know if the horse has dominant genes? You'll have to check the record of his offspring for what you suspect are inheritable traits. Even then, it's just a guess.

Inbreeding, the mating of closely related animals, is a method of producing homozygously dominant horses.

However, inbreeding has its drawbacks and is not for the average horseowner.

Linebreeding is a special form of inbreeding, which attempts to emphasize the influence of a single ancestor in the pedigree, and can be very helpful to the average horeseowner.

Outbreeding is the mating of individuals not closely related in the last three or four generations, and is probably the best system for the breeder of fewer than 10 or 12 mares.

It is to be hoped that our quick study of genetics has demonstrated the complexities of the subject and has you a bit confused as to the results you can expect.

Based on the confusion and complexities I have wrought, the laws of probability say my recommendations should now be followed by 87 percent of the readers. Consequently:

1. Select a brood mare and stallion that please you in both appearance and performance records.
2. Considering just the stallion and the mare, breed the best performer to the best performer in your field of interest. That's the law of selectivity; it's also your best chance for good results.
3. Understand that the study of genetics proves "what you see ain't necessarily what you get."
4. Continue to study genetics so you can be as confused and unsure as the best experts, and maybe it'll result in the much-needed further study of the horse.

Don't Boil Water or Spank Bottoms!

It's foaling time. Ah, the joy of being a new parent. Even if that funny, long-legged baby does have silly, crooked whiskers.

The birth of a foal is a beautiful and exciting experience, but there can be danger too.

Understanding the foaling process eliminates some of the dangers, while unskilled or untimely assistance increases the chances of disease or even death for the foal, the mare, or both.

Dr. Byrd suggests you do little to assist nature.

"Nature does a pretty good job on her own. And in too many cases, an overly helpful owner creates problems where there were none."

He recommends you have three things on hand at foaling time:

1. A bottle of iodine
2. Some clean towels
3. A clean, dry, sheltered area for the mare and foal

The iodine is to be poured on the foal's navel cord just after the cord breaks. This is extremely important, since navel infection is very common among foals. The cord represents a direct passage to the foal's bladder and to the blood supply to the liver. Any infection that gets into this passage is transmitted to the rest of the foal's system and can easily result in "joint, or navel ill," a severe disease that may cause death.

The clean towels are used to dry the foal after birth. It isn't necessary that you do this, but, especially in cold weather, drying the foal keeps it from becoming chilled and gets the little one's circulation going.

If the weather is nice, the best place for the mare to foal is a grassy pasture. But if you want the mare sheltered, be sure to put her in your biggest stall. Both straw and wood shavings make good bedding for the mare and foal.

Now that you're prepared, let's check the sequence of events.

The average pregnancy is 342 days, give or take 10 days. As foaling time approaches, look for telltale signs. The mare's milk glands will enlarge and a waxy substance may develop on the ends of the nipples. Milk may drip or stream from the nipples, a good indication foaling will occur within 15 minutes to 48 hours.

As the time nears, the mare will exhibit nervousness, showing all the signs of colic, for indeed, she does have stomach cramps.

The water bag will appear and break. Don't be concerned; it's natural that there will be lots of water. In 15 minutes or less, the foal's front feet should appear. In a normal birth presentation, the foal's head will be between the front feet. It is not uncommon for the mare to get up and walk around before the birth is complete. From the time the feet first appear, it will take from 2 to 10 minutes for the remainder of the birth process.

Let a normal birth take place, advises Dr. Byrd. Your main job as the observer is to look for signs of an abnormal birth presentation.

If anything other than the two front feet and the head should appear, or if nothing appears after 15 minutes of hard labor, call your vet, describe exactly what you see and follow his instructions carefully.

If the sack is still over the foal's head after the birth process is complete, stick your fingers through the membrane at the foal's mouth, then pull the sack back away from his nostrils so the foal can breathe. Don't do anything else until the mare has cleaned the foal and both are relaxed. Pour the iodine on the foal's navel cord and rub the foal with the clean towels.

It will take from five minutes to three hours for the mare to expel all the afterbirth. Collect the afterbirth so it may be checked by the vet.

When the foal decides it's time for a drink, he'll try to get to his feet; this can take from 15 minutes to an hour. You'll want to ease his struggle, but don't. The exercise is good for the foal.

The foal should be nursing within two hours. If he isn't, then a little assistance may be helpful. But don't ry to push the foal toward the mare. He won't go. Stand on the opposite side of the mare from the foal and try to get the foal to suck on your fingers. Then guide him toward the milk. A little squirt on his nose will get his attention.

The foal should pass the meconium from the rectum shortly after having a good drink of milk, says Dr. Byrd. If the foal shows signs of straining, tail elevation, or cramping, call the veterinarian. Do not give the foal an enema yourself.

Within 12 hours of foaling, have your vet check both the mare and foal and administer disease-preventing medication to both.

As simple as it is, that's the wonderful miracle of foaling.

Someone Must Be a Good Mommie

The chances are good that sooner or later you will be involved with the care of an orphaned foal or a foal whose mother is not producing enough milk.

Don't panic. Getting prepared and caring for the new baby is easier than it may appear at first. After all, there are no diapers to change and no burping is required.

In sequence of importance, doing everything possible to keep the baby healthy should be your primary concern.

The first step is to make certain the foal's navel cord stump has been well saturated with iodine as soon as possible after foaling. This helps keep infection from entering the foal's system.

Your second step is to provide the foal with colostrum, providing the mother cannot do it. Colostrum is in the mare's first milk, that which is produced during the first 12 hours after foaling. The colostrum contains antibodies the mare has built up to protect the foal from disease.

If the mare dies before the foal gets the colostrum, it is strongly advised that another mare that has just foaled be found and milk be supplied by her. In most cases, this is virually impossible and in my opinion, a time-consuming frustration. I recommend you call your veterinarian, who will administer antibiotics and vitamins.

What will really make the foal happy and healthy is something to eat.

There are commercially produced milk replacers just for foals. These are probably your best bet. They are designed especially for this purpose and are readily available through local feed stores. Such milk replacers are relatively inexpensive and easy to use.

Then there are the old-time, mix-it-yourself formulas.

A little snack, which should be fed to the foal in a baby bottle six to eight times around the clock during the first 10 days, is prepared by using two pints of low-fat cow's milk (about three percent fat), a half-pint of warm water, 1.5 ounces of corn syrup, one to two ounces of limewater, two shots of cod liver oil, and a pinch of bone flour. The ingredients are easy to find, with the possible exception of limewater.

Limewater, which is a solution of slaked lime (lime that has had the chemical balance changed) is used to counteract an acid condition. For foals, the acid condition would be known as colic. Limewater will be found at most pharmacies, but will not be stocked by your chain-operated drug stores.

A little simpler formula can be made by using one pint of low-fat cow's milk, four ounces of limewater, and two teaspoons of corn syrup. A half-pint of this formula should be fed every hour on the hour for the first four or five days. After that, increase the amount to a little more than a pint and feed every two hours.

Commercially prepared milk replacers for human babies can be fed to orphaned foals, but they must be diluted with water by about one half.

My preference is to find a fresh nanny goat, stand her on a bale of hay and let her gradually assume the duties of motherhood. If you introduce the foal and goat to one another carefully every hour during the first day, both will usually get the idea and carry on naturally from there.

Mamma goat will jump onto the bale of hay each time baby horse wants a snack and you can go your merry way concentrating on other chores and anticipating a good night's sleep.

One other tip about orphaned foals. The best place for them is out in the sunshine in a pasture where they can get plenty of healthy exercise.

And curb your motherly instincts. You'll find the orphaned foal is destined to be a spoiled brat without a great deal of assistance.

Out on His Own

There comes a time in the life of every litte girl and boy horse when it's necessary to say "Good-bye, Momma."

Weaning time is arriving earlier and earlier in the lives of horses. Years ago it was common practice to leave a foal with the mare for at least six months. Today, most foals, under average conditions, are weaned at four months. There is a definite move toward weaning at three months, and I believe foals weaned at two months do quite well.

Mares are not particularly good milk producers, and with our improved feeding and handling techniques, I'm sure there is little nutritional danger involved with early weaning.

However, I prefer to determine the time of weaning according to circumstances that have little to do with the foal's age. I shorten or lengthen the time the foal is with the mare based on the disposition and characteristics of the mare.

If I really like the disposition of the mare, I may leave the foal with her for a full four months. If the mare is cranky, or has characteristics I don't like, I wean the foal as early as possible — two months.

I'm a firm believer the foal will have more or less of the mare's traits depending on the length of time they are together.

When you decide to wean, plan ahead; be sure you are prepared.

There are two basic ways of weaning.

You can take the mare and foal to the barn, put the foal in a stall, and then return the mare to the pasture, or, if you happen to have several mares and foals, you can remove a couple of the dams, leaving the foals to play and seek solace with their companions.

Circumstances may dictate the method used, but in any case, the key element is to get the mare and foal separated by as great a distance as possible. If they can see each other, or call to each other, the weaning is going to be much more traumatic and dangerous for both. When they can see or talk to each other, they will often attempt to get back together, even if it means going over, under, or through the fencing.

I like to prepare a stall for the mare and foal the night before weaning, then allow the foal to accept the stall while Momma is there. In the morning, I take the mare back to pasture without Junior.

Check on the foal every hour or so to see he isn't getting too overheated, or cast, or injured from bouncing around the stall.

Keep grain and hay in front of the foal at all times. The foal probably won't eat much, but even if he does, there is little danger it will hurt him.

Part of the planning should include a check on the water supply for the foal. If the barn has automatic waterers, low enough, fine. If water buckets are used, they should not be left on the stall floor where they will be knocked over, or become a source of injury.

Once the weaning is accomplished, Momma isn't going to get her ration of grain, and I even cut back on her hay for a few days. It is also a good idea to limit the amount of water she is allowed. Three gallons every eight hours is about right.

Check the mare's udder frequently, if it gets too tight and hot, rub gently with camphorated oil. Do not milk the mare as this only prolongs the drying process.

The cutback in feed and water, plus the camphorated oil, and the normal amount of exercise she'll take on her own, should be enough to avoid most problems.

The checks on Momma need not be as frequent as those on Baby, and usually it isn't necessary to spend much time reassuring her. Baby, however, may need three or four talk and groom sessions before he settles.

Just before bedtime I like to check the mare, then the foal. You can give the foal a cube of sugar, and tuck him in. If he cries and whines during the early part of the evening, be brave. Tomorrow, he'll be all grown-up.

So You'll Know Your Horse

I believe in music, love, friendship, and that everything and everyone has an influence on everything and everyone. I believe the sun, the moon and the stars influence each of us, and our horses.

I recently wrote a series of articles for *Horse and Horseman* magazine entitled "The Zodiac Horse." The series touched off a major controversy. I've been called everything from a prophet to a Satan worshipper.

I'm neither.

The opinions were nearly equally divided. Some said the material wasn't worth two cents. Others said it was the best understanding of their horses they had ever encountered.

For what it's worth, here's a quick synopsis of the 12 signs of the zodiac. Compare your horse's personality to his sign. If it's accurate, great, If not, it's still fun.

CAPRICORN, December 22 to January 19. This horse is always interested in the practical, organized, logical approach. He has a sense of his own worth, and his training must proceed along a well-planned path. A consistent teaching approach works well, while lavish praise or force will not work at all. The Capricorn horse is a natural "trail horse," being a born investigator.

AQUARIUS, January 20 to February 19. This horse is quick to learn anything, and in his natural field, be it jumping or reining, he'll seem to understand the challenges even before he has had formal schooling. The Aquarius horse loves independence and can't be stalled for days on end. He needs to be turned out frequently if he is to remain fresh and creative.

PISCES, February 20 to March 20. There are two sides to this horse's nature, and both are powerful. The Pisces horse does not normally make a good pleasure horse. He may be a brilliant mover, but he can't stand the mental boredom. Let him do work that challenges his talents. His fluid personality can't be forced into a rigid pattern.

ARIES, March 21 to April 20. This horse loves to take the lead. He is a natural race horse, endurance horse, or three-day eventer. Because the Aries horse is self-assertive, his handler must be prepared to "lock horns" with him occasionally. The Aries horse is bold, sometimes difficult to handle.

TAURUS, April 21 to May 21. This horse will not be rushed into anything. He likes the status quo and is usually very content, but don't provoke him. He doesn't learn quickly because he doesn't like change. But teach him an exercise and he'll never forget it. He makes a very good show horse at almost any event.

GEMINI, May 22 to June 21. This horse is versatile, adaptable, and inquisitive, with a very changeable disposition. He is capable of learning a good deal, and he is usually very good at whatever it is you give him to do. But, because he can master so much, he falls into his own trap — too much too soon.

CANCER, June 22 to July 23. This horse tends to yield, bend, and flow around opposition. He is a master at passive resistance. You can't force him to learn or work.

When handled correctly, you'll find this horse a super friend and willing worker. He's tough on the outside, but a big softie on the inside. Enjoy him!

LEO, July 24 to August 23. The Leo horse is honest, inspired, and truly gifted. Occasionally pompous and hard to train, he is also playful, loyal, and lovable.

The Leo horse is a natural show horse. He likes to "shine." Of all horses, Leo horses need the most tender loving care, and they perform in appreciation.

VIRGO, August 24 to September 23. For this horse, material comforts are extremely important. A good stall, good food, and a good blanket are important. Treat him right, and he'll treat you right. This horse will give his very best in every performance. However, because he is so willing to give, he expects the same from his rider. He is quick to anger if he knows more than his handler.

LIBRA, September 24 to October 23. This horse has a great sense of give and take. He makes an excellent Western horse because he can work on his own, and he makes a good English horse since he can compromise well with his rider. Of all signs, Libra has the most versatility.

SCORPIO, October 24 to November 22. Very capable of showing explosive anger, this horse will kick, bite, and strike. On the other hand, he is among the greatest performers. It is not unusual for the Scorpio horse to be more talented than the handler.

If taken in the direction of natural talents, the Scorpio is a sure champion. If taken in the wrong direction, he will be a flop. This horse is often saint or sinner.

SAGITTARIUS, November 23 to December 21. This horse is a natural athlete and must have plenty of work to remain healthy. He does best in events that are strenuous, such as jumping, racing, or polo.

Sagittarius horses hate to be bossed and will not succumb to force. Ask him nicely and he'll be dynamic.

Be Smart, Geld

There are too many bad stallions around.

And too few good ones.

I'm not just talking about backyard stallions. I'm talking about a lot of bad stallions in the show ring, on the race track, and at ranches.

And when I say bad, I'm not referring to disposition or manners. I'm referring to conformation and ability to perform.

Why, oh why, do so many people insist on keeping so many poorly conformed, poorly bred, tangle-footed, jug-headed, slow pokes as stallions? I won't even mention all the ill-tempered, bad-mannered studs I've seen. I blame their behavior on their handlers, even though I know some of it is hereditary.

There are three good reasons to geld a horse.

1. Bad geldings don't perpetuate themselves, while bad stallions do, thereby lowering the quality of horses.
2. Geldings are normally easier to handle and have definitely savaged fewer owners.
3. Good geldings are good for the horse business, while bad stallions are bad for business. Bad stallions produce horses of low quality, and therefore low price, and sometimes, due to low breeding fees, they keep some nice mares from going to some nice stallions.

Keeping a poorly conformed, poorly bred horse as a stallion

guarantees only one thing: the majority of his offspring will be poorly conformed and poorly bred.

Usually, gelding a horse makes him easier to handle, easier to train, and easier on himself. I've seen many a good stallion that would have been fantastic as a performance gelding if only his owner had had the good sense to help him.

As a stallion, the famous race horse, Kelso, was nothing. As a gelding, he was acclaimed horse of the century.

I've been told that a lot of would-be horsemen can't adjust psychologically to the idea of gelding a horse. I believe there's some truth to it. But I've yet to meet a real horseman who wouldn't say, "Cut that horse," when he can see it is best for the horse, the breed, the owner, and the industry.

I have a feeling the same psychological problem holds true in a little different way for many women. I think a lot of would-be horsewomen idolize their tangle-footed, ill-conformed studs.

But then, some people never learn.

"A good gelding is always better than a bad stallion." Words of wisdom.

Guardian Angels Protect Horses and Horseowners

I know there are guardian angels.

If there weren't, there would be half as many horses and 80 percent fewer horsemen.

"This horse has never made a bad move," she commented with a smile as she climbed aboard bareback and rode away using only a halter and lead rope."

Somewhere along the trail, the horse made a bad move. The X-rays showed only a tiny pelvic fracture. The soreness, they promised, would go away in a week or two.

"My daughter's horse never kicks," one mother told another.

The lawsuit is pending. The friend is mending, slowly. The horse hasn't kicked since.

"My horse loves me," she said, giving the horse a hug around the neck. "I know he'd never do anything to hurt me."

The cut above the eye will leave only a small scar. The one on the nose is doing just fine. She bought a new pair of sun glasses.

I can't believe it, but I see barefoot kids working around horses all the time. The other day, I watched a woman sit down on the grass not a foot away from her horse's hindquarters. Luckily, the horse only jumped sideways and the one hoof that did hit her only bruised her leg.

Why do we persist in this madness?

Because familiarity breeds contempt. We tend to be much less cautious around horses we know than those we don't. That seems to be human nature.

What we must do to reduce accidents is remain alert to the horse's nature, whether we know him or not.

The horse is a timid animal. He has difficulty in seeing things well, and would sooner run than stay and investigate.

It is seldom that a horse will intentionally do anything to hurt you. The wreck nearly always happens as a result of the horse trying to get away from something he fears, whether the danger is real or imaginary. The injury results from the fact that the horse is enormously strong, weighs 1,000 pounds or more, has very hard hoofs that are likely to be shod, and doesn't reason too well.

If he decides to occupy the same space I'm occupying, he usually does, since I'm skinny and don't move too fast.

In addition to accidents happening most frequently with the horses we know well, they are more likely to happen when we are performing routine tasks.

We tie a horse when we are going to groom him, saddle or unsaddle him, or go back to the tack room for something we forgot. We expect the horse to stand there quietly, and in most cases he does. After a while, we become a little careless.

We start tying the horse by the reins, or we don't tie a slip knot, or we tie the horse to an object that is too low or too weak, or we tie him in a congested area. Then the accident happens.

If we're lucky and don't get hurt, the horse usually does, and then we say, "Gee, I never should have tied him there."

Carelessness in leading a horse is common. Even the best-natured, best-trained horse should be led up next to you so you can see his head and ears. In that position, you have a fighting chance.

If the horse walks behind you at the end of five feet of lead rope, it's more likely he'll jump on you, bite you, run over you, or jerk you off your feet.

Of course, everyone knows you should never wrap a lead rope around your hand or arm or neck. But many still foolishly tempt fate.

Yes! It's the horses we know the best and love the most, the ones that would never hurt us, that do.

But until it happens, you won't get anyone to believe it.

And that's why horsemen have guardian angels.

I sure hope they have a "no strike" clause in their heavenly contract.

EQUINE HEALTH RECORD

NAME_____ IDENT _____ COLOR _____

BIRTH DATE _____ SEX ____ OWNER _____

CHRONIC PROBLEMS _____

DRUG ALLERGIES _____

_____

VACCINATION RECORD

Tetanus Toxoid	Encephalomyelitis					

WORMING RECORD

Date	Method	Drug	Date	Method	Drug	Date	Method	Drug

LABORATORY TESTS

Date	Test	Results

RECOMMENDED HEALTH PROCEDURES

Worming:

Horses One Year or Older — Treatment for all worms twice a year (Dec.-June). Treatment for bloodworms (Strongyles) orally in feed every 8 weeks.

Foals — First worming at 2-3 months. Repeat at 3 month intervals.

Broodmares — Twice a year, generally Nov.-Dec. and midsummer. Do not worm after 9 months of pregnancy except for specially selected treatment.

Vaccination:

Tetanus Antitoxin — Duration of protection not more than 10 days. To be given following injury to an animal that has not received tetanus toxoid.

Tetanus Toxoid — Duration of protection at least 1 year. Two injections 30-60 days apart. Booster given yearly.

Encephalomyelitis (Sleeping Sickness) — Duration of protection for season of infection. Two injections 7-14 days apart during May-July. (This and tetanus toxoid vaccination to start at about 4 months of age.

Teeth:

Saddle & Breeding Animals — Check yearly. Float if necessary.

Racing Animals — Check and float twice a year.

Foaling Mares:

Mare — Tetanus antitoxin or toxoid.

Foal — Tetanus antitoxin or toxoid and penn strep-enema if needed.

BREEDING RECORD

Estrus Date		Date Bred	Pregnancy Exam.		Comments
In Date	Out Date		Date	Diagnosis	

DIAGNOSIS AND TREATMENT RECORD

Date	Diagnosis	Treatment and Remarks

MISCELLANEOUS INFORMATION

Date	Remarks

SHOEING AND TRIMMING RECORD   *T-Trim   S-Shoe

*	Date	*	Date	*	Date	*	Date	*	Date	*	Date	*	Date

Special Shoeing Requirements: _____